Advancing Maths for AQA
MECHANICS 4

Ted Graham, Aidan Burrows and Brian Gaulter

Series editors
Roger Williamson   Sam Boardman   Graham Eaton
Ted Graham   Keith Parramore

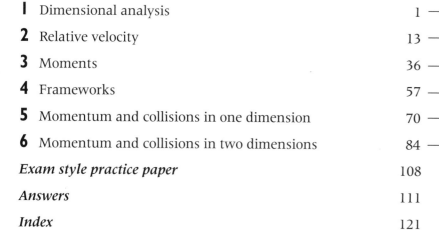

Heinemann

Heinemann Educational Publishers
a division of Heinemann Publishers (Oxford) Ltd,
Halley Court, Jordan Hill, Oxford OX2 8EJ

OXFORD   JOHANNESBURG   BLANTYRE   MELBOURNE
AUCKLAND   SINGAPORE   GABORONE   PORTSMOUTH NH (USA)
CHICAGO

First published in 2001

06   05   04   03   02
10   9   8   7   6   5   4   3   2   1

ISBN 0 435 51309 5

Cover design by Miller, Craig and Cocking

Typeset and illustrated by Tech-Set Limited, Gateshead, Tyne & Wear

Printed and bound by Scotprint

Acknowledgements
The publishers and authors acknowledge the work of the writers, Ray Atkin,
John Berry, Sam Boardman, David Burghes, Derek Collins, Tim Cross,
Ted Graham, Phil Rawlins, Tom Roper, Rob Summerson and Elwyn Williams of
the *AEB Mathematics for AS and A-Level Series*, from which some exercises and
examples have been taken.

The publishers' and authors' thanks are due to the AQA for the permission to
reproduce questions from past examination papers.

The answers have been provided by the authors and are not the responsibility
of the examining board.

About this book

This book is one in a series of textbooks designed to provide you with exceptional preparation for AQA's new Advanced GCE Specification B. The series authors are all senior members of the examining team and have prepared the textbooks specifically to support you in studying this course.

Finding your way around

The following are there to help you find your way around when you are studying and revising:

- **edge marks** (shown on the front page) – these help you to get to the right chapter quickly;
- **contents list** – this identifies the individual sections dealing with key syllabus concepts so that you can go straight to the areas that you are looking for;
- **index** – a number in bold type indicates where to find the main entry for that topic.

Key points

Key points are not only summarised at the end of each chapter but are also boxed and highlighted within the text like this:

> The dimensions of a quantity can be found by using either
> - its definition, or
> - a formula in which it is involved.

Exercises and exam questions

Worked examples and carefully graded questions familiarise you with the specification and bring you up to exam standard. Each book contains:

- Worked examples and Worked exam questions to show you how to tackle typical questions; Examiner's tips will also provide guidance;
- Graded exercises, gradually increasing in difficulty up to exam-level questions, which are marked by an [A];
- Test-yourself sections for each chapter so that you can check your understanding of the key aspects of that chapter and identify any sections that you should review;
- Answers to the questions are included at the end of the book.

Unless otherwise stated, where a numerical value is required, assume $g = 9.8 \, \mathrm{m \, s^{-2}}$.

Learning objectives

After studying this chapter you should be able to:

- find dimensions of quantities
- check formulae for consistency
- predict formulae, which connect particular variables in given circumstances.

1.1 Introduction

In mechanics nearly all quantities are expressed in terms of units. In many cases more than one representation is possible.

For example, by using $F = ma$ we can write $1\,N = kg\,m\,s^{-2}$ or by considering the units for moments we can write $1\,N\,m = 1\,kg\,m^2\,s^{-2}$.

However, we can express quantities in terms of three fundamental, independent dimensions, mass, length and time (denoted by M, L and T). The advantage of doing this is that this representation is unique.

There are two main uses of such analysis:

- equations can be checked for consistency,
- formulae, which link certain variables, can be predicted. (The method of dimensional analysis.)

Dimensions of quantities

The dimensions of a quantity can be found by using either

- its definition, or
- a formula in which it is involved.

The notation $[x]$ will be used to denote the dimensions of x, which will be given in terms of M, L and T.

Worked example 1.1

Find the dimensions of:

(a) speed,

(b) acceleration,

(c) force,

(d) the coefficient of friction.

Solution

(a) $[v] = [\text{speed}] = \dfrac{[\text{distance}]}{[\text{time}]} = \dfrac{L}{T} = LT^{-1}$

Note that velocity is a vector quantity but its dimensions are those of its magnitude.

(b) $[a] = \dfrac{[\text{change in velocity}]}{[\text{time}]} = \dfrac{LT^{-1}}{T} = LT^{-2}$

(c) $F = ma \Rightarrow [F] = [m] \times [a] = MLT^{-2}$

> The dimensions of a product are equal to the product of dimensions:
>
> i.e. $[ab] = [a] \times [b]$

(d) The coefficient of friction, μ, can be found using $F_{\text{max}} = \mu R$.

$[F_{\text{max}}] = [\mu] \times [R]$

$MLT^{-2} = [\mu] \times MLT^{-2} \Rightarrow [\mu] = 1$
This implies that μ is dimensionless.

There are many other constants and variables in mechanics which are dimensionless.

The next example shows that any angle is dimensionless.

Worked example 1.2

The formula for the arc length of a circle is $s = r\theta$. Find the dimensions of θ.

Solution

$[s] = [r] \times [\theta] \Rightarrow L = L \times [\theta] \Rightarrow [\theta] = 1$

So θ is dimensionless.

Worked example 1.3

Newton's law of gravitation states that the force of attraction between two particles is given by,

$$F = \frac{Gm_1 m_2}{d^2}$$

where m_1 and m_2 are the masses of the two particles and d is the distance between them.

Find the dimensions of G.

Solution

Rearranging the formula gives,

$$G = \frac{Fd^2}{m_1 m_2}$$

$$[G] = \frac{\text{MLT}^{-2} \times \text{L}^2}{\text{M}^2} = \text{M}^{-1}\text{L}^3\text{T}^{-2}$$

Worked example 1.4

Simple Harmonic Motion is defined by $a = -\omega^2 x$, where a is the acceleration, x is the displacement and ω is a constant. Find the dimensions of ω.

Solution

First consider a, the acceleration, which has dimensions LT^{-2}.

$$[a] = [\omega]^2 \times [x]$$

$$\text{LT}^{-2} = [\omega]^2\text{L} \Rightarrow [\omega]^2 = \text{T}^{-2} \Rightarrow [\omega] = \text{T}^{-1}$$

Dimensions of derivatives

Velocity, which is given by $\dfrac{dx}{dt}$, has dimensions $\dfrac{\text{L}}{\text{T}}$. In general a derivative is the limit of the ratio of two small changes, hence

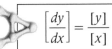

$$\left[\frac{dy}{dx}\right] = \frac{[y]}{[x]}$$

Worked example 1.5

The angular velocity and angular acceleration of a particle moving in a plane are defined by $\dfrac{d\theta}{dt}$ and $\dfrac{d^2\theta}{dt^2}$ respectively. Find their dimensions.

Solution

$$\left[\frac{d\theta}{dt}\right] = \frac{[\theta]}{[t]} = \frac{1}{\text{T}} = \text{T}^{-1}$$

$$\left[\frac{d^2\theta}{dt^2}\right] = \frac{\left[\dfrac{d\theta}{dt}\right]}{[t]} = \frac{\dfrac{1}{\text{T}}}{\text{T}} = \text{T}^{-2}$$

Consistency of equations

Two quantities, which have different dimensions, cannot be added: for example, $2 \text{ cm}^2 + 3 \text{ cm}^3$ cannot be combined.

> If $[a] + [b] = [c]$ than a, b and c must all have the same dimensions.

Worked example 1.6

Show that the equations $s = vt - \frac{1}{2}at^2$ is dimensionally consistent.

Solution

If the equation is consistent then $[s] = [vt] = [\frac{1}{2}at^2]$.

$$[s] = L$$

$$[vt] = [v] \times [t] = \frac{L}{T} \times T = L$$

$$[\tfrac{1}{2}at^2] = [at^2] = [a] \times [t]^2 = \frac{L}{T^2} \times T^2 = L$$

Hence the equation is consistent.

Note that because an equation is dimensionally consistent, this doesn't necessarily make it valid.

Worked example 1.7

It is believed that the motion of a rocket, t seconds after blast off, can be modelled by the equation,

$$\frac{dv}{dt} = -g + \frac{kU}{M_0 - kt}$$

where M_0 is the initial mass of the rocket, U is the speed of the ejected fuel relative to the rocket, and v is the velocity of the rocket at time t. Find the dimensions of k, if the equation is dimensionally consistent.

Solution

The denominator $M_0 - kt$ must be consistent, so $[M_0] = [kt]$.

$$M = [k]T \Rightarrow [k] = \frac{M}{T} = MT^{-1}$$

Also,

$$\left[\frac{dv}{dt}\right] = \frac{[v]}{[t]} = \frac{\dfrac{L}{T}}{T} = \frac{L}{T^2}$$

$$[g] = \frac{L}{T^2}$$

$$\left[\frac{kU}{M_0 - kt}\right] = \frac{[k] \times [U]}{[M_0]} = \frac{\dfrac{M}{T} \times \dfrac{L}{T}}{M} = \frac{L}{T^2}$$

Hence the equation is dimensionally consistent if

$$[k] = \frac{M}{T} = MT^{-1}.$$

Dimensions of trigonometric functions

Any trigonometric ratio is defined as the ratio of two sides. This means that $\sin \theta$, $\cos \theta$ and $\tan \theta$ are dimensionless. Furthermore, θ must also be dimensionless.

| $\sin x$, $\cos x$ and $\tan x$ are all dimensionless. |

Worked example 1.8

The displacement, x, of a particle, at time t, is described by the expression

$$x = A \sin (\omega t + C) + B.$$

Find the dimensions of the constants A, B, C and ω.

Solution

The term $\omega t + C$ must be dimensionless, hence $[\omega] = T^{-1}$ and C must be dimensionless.

Finally, for consistency, $[A] = [B] = [x] = L$.

EXERCISE 1A

1 Find the dimensions of each of the following quantities, which are commonly used in mechanics. Mass is represented by m, velocity by v, acceleration by g, height by h, force by F, time by t, and area by A.

(a) Kinetic energy E, given by $E = \frac{1}{2}mv^2$.

(b) Potential energy P, given by $P = mgh$.

(c) Impulse I, given by $I = Ft$.

(d) Pressure P, given by $P = \dfrac{F}{A}$.

(e) Density ρ, given by ρ = mass per unit volume.

(f) Density ρ, given by ρ = mass per unit area.

2 Hooke's law can be written $T = \dfrac{\lambda x}{l}$, where T is the tension in an elastic string of natural length l, and x is the extension produced. Find the dimensions of the modulus of elasticity λ, and the dimensions of E, given by $E = \dfrac{\lambda x^2}{2l}$.

3 Which of the following equations are dimensionally consistent? (Note that each variable represents the same quantity in each part of this question.)

(a) $t = \dfrac{v - u}{a}$, where time is represented by t, acceleration by a, and velocity by u and v.

(b) $s = \dfrac{v^2 - u^2}{2a}$, where distance is represented by s.

(c) $t = \pi \sqrt{\dfrac{l^3}{g}}$, where length is represented by l and acceleration by g.

(d) $F = \dfrac{mu^2}{l} - mg(2 - 3 \cos \theta)$, where force is represented by F, and θ is an angle.

4 The acceleration, a, of a body falling at speed v, is modelled by the equation,

$$a = g - kv^2.$$

Find the dimensions of the constant k, which will make the equation dimensionally consistent.

5 The height, h, at which a hover mower moves over the ground, is thought to depend on the volume of air, F, which is pumped per second through the fan, and on the speed, u, at which the air escapes from under the mower apron. Show that h, F and u could be related by the equation $h = k \sqrt{\dfrac{F}{u}}$.

6 Find the dimensions of the constants A, B and k in each of the following cases, where x represents displacement, v represents velocity and a represents acceleration:

(a) $x = A \cos (kt + B)$,

(b) $x = At + Bt^2$,

(c) $a = A \sin (kt) + B$,

(d) $Ax + Bv + a = 0$.

1.2 The method of dimensional analysis

> The dimensions M, L and T are independent, so if it is known that
>
> $$M^aL^bT^c = M^\alpha L^\beta T^\gamma$$
>
> then for consistency, the following simultaneous equations must hold,
>
> $$a = \alpha, \qquad b = \beta \qquad \text{and} \qquad c = \gamma.$$

These equations are useful for predicting formulae, which link given variables in particular circumstances.

Worked example 1.9

To model the period, P, of a simple pendulum it is suggested that

$$P = km^al^bg^c$$

where m is the mass of the bob, l is the length of the string and k is a dimensionless constant. Find the values of a, b and c.

Solution

$$[P] = T$$

$$[g] = LT^{-2}$$

$$T = M^aL^b(LT^{-2})^c$$

$$\Rightarrow M^0L^0T^1 = M^aL^{b+c}T^{-2c}$$

Equating powers of M, L and T on both sides of this equation gives,

$$0 = a$$

$$0 = b + c$$

$$1 = -2c$$

These equations produce $c = -\frac{1}{2}$, $b = \frac{1}{2}$ and $a = 0$. The model is therefore given by,

$$P = km^0l^{\frac{1}{2}}g^{-\frac{1}{2}} \Rightarrow P = k\sqrt{\frac{l}{g}}.$$

The value of the constant k can be estimated using experimental data. In reality k itself is a function of the greatest angle between the string and the vertical. This doesn't conflict with k being dimensionless, because we have shown that angles are dimensionless.

Worked example 1.10

The gravitational force between two masses, m_1 and m_2, is given by

$$\frac{Gm_1m_2}{d^2}$$

where G is a constant and d is the distance between the centres of the two bodies.

A body is projected vertically from the earth's surface. When air resistance is neglected, the critical velocity of escape (denoted by v) is given by

$$v = kG^aE^bR^c$$

where E is the mass of the planet and R is the radius of the planet.

(a) Find the values of a, b and c.

(b) It is known that the escape velocity from earth is approximately 1.12×10^4 m s^{-1}. The earth's radius is about 6370 km and its mass is about 5.96×10^{24} kg, and the value of G is about 6.67×10^{-11} kg^{-1} m^3 s^{-2}. Estimate k.

(c) If the mass of the moon is 7.34×10^{22} kg and its radius is 1740 km, estimate the escape velocity from the moon.

Solution

(a) From the units given for the value of G in the question (or from Worked example 1.3),

$$[G] = M^{-1}L^3T^{-2}.$$

Also $[E] = M$, $[R] = L$

and $[v] = LT^{-1}$

$$[v] = [G]^a[E]^b[R]^c = (M^{-1}L^3T^{-2})^a(M)^b(L)^c$$

$$M^0L^1T^{-1} = M^{b-a}L^{3a+c}T^{-2a}$$

Equating powers of M, L and T gives,

$$0 = b - a$$

$$1 = 3a + c$$

$$-1 = -2a$$

From these equations we get $a = b = \frac{1}{2}$ and $c = -\frac{1}{2}$.

(b) Hence the escape velocity takes the form

$$v = k\sqrt{\frac{GE}{R}}.$$

We now substitute $v = 1.12 \times 10^4$ m s^{-1}, $R = 6.37 \times 10^6$ m, $E = 5.96 \times 10^{24}$ kg and $G = 6.67 \times 10^{-11}$ kg^{-1} m^3 s^{-2}. This gives $k = 1.42$ (3 sf).

(c) Substituting $E = 7.34 \times 10^{22}$ kg, $R = 1.74 \times 10^{6}$ m and $G = 6.67 \times 10^{-11}$ kg^{-1} m^{3} s^{-2}, gives the escape velocity from the moon as,

$$v = 2.38 \times 10^{3} \text{ m s}^{-1}.$$

EXERCISE 1B

1 The frequency, f, of a note given by a wind instrument depends on its length, l, the air pressure, p (force per unit area), and the air density, d. If f is proportional to $l^x p^y d^z$ find the values of x, y and z. Note that frequency has dimensions T^{-1}.

2 A bottle that is partially submerged in water oscillates up and down. Assume that the period of the oscillations depends on the density of the water, ρ, the acceleration due to gravity, g, and the area of the base of the bottle, A.

  (a) Use dimensional analysis to find an expression for the period of the oscillations of the bottle in terms ρ, g, A and a dimensionless constant k.

  (b) If the period of the oscillations for a bottle of base area 16 cm^2 is 0.2 s find k.

  (c) The base of the bottle is circular. How would doubling the radius of the base of the bottle affect the period?　[A]

3 Find the values of x, y and z in the following expression:

$$M^{-1}LT^7 = (M^2LT)^x(M^{-2}L^{-1}T^2)^y(ML^2T^{-1})^z$$

4 It is known that the frequency, f, of a stretched piano wire depends on its length, l, the tension, T, in the wire, and the density, ρ, of the wire (where ρ is the mass per unit length).

  (a) Use dimensional analysis to find the relationship between these quantities.

  (b) What will be the effect on the frequency of a particular wire if the tension in the wire is doubled?

5 Three physical quantities X, Y and Z have dimensions $M^p L^q T^r$, $ML^{-2}T^2$, and ML^2T respectively. Find the constants p, q and r, given that $X = \dfrac{Y}{Z}$.

6 Pressure in a liquid varies with depth. Pressure, P, can be defined as $\dfrac{\text{force}}{\text{area}}$. Use dimensional analysis to find an expression for P in terms of the acceleration due to gravity, g, the depth of the liquid, h, the density of the liquid, ρ, and a dimensionless constant k.

7   Imagine that a particle of mass m is dropped into a tunnel which passes straight through the centre of the earth. If air resistance is neglected the particle will oscillate backwards and forwards along the diameter. Use dimensional analysis to find a formula for the period of the oscillation, P, in terms of the radius of the earth, R, the mass of the earth, M, the gravitational constant, G (as defined in Worked example 1.10), and a dimensionless constant k.

8   A pendulum consists of a string of length l m and a small sphere of mass m kg. A student attempts to find an expression for the period T s of the motion of the pendulum by using dimensional analysis. He initially assumes that

   $$T = kl^x g^y m^z$$

   where k is a dimensionless constant, and the values of x, y and z are to be found by the student.

   (a) Use dimensional analysis to show that $z = 0$, and find the values of x and y.

   (b) The student then conducts an experiment with a pendulum of length 0.4 m and observes that the period is approximately 1.3 s. Use the student's results to find k and hence predict the period of a pendulum of length 0.9 m.   [A]

9   A student is formulating a mathematical model to predict the period of the vibrations of a guitar string. She assumes that the period depends on the length of the string, l, the tension in the string, S, and the mass of the string, m. She then states that

   Period $\propto m^a l^b S^c$.

   Determine the values of a, b and c in this model so that it is dimensionally consistent.   [A]

10 A tank of water has a small hole at its base through which water escapes at speed v. A possible model to predict the speed at which the water leaves the tank is

   $$v = kh^a g^b \rho^c$$

   where h is the depth of water in the tank, g is the acceleration due to gravity, ρ is the density of the water and k is a dimensionless constant.

   (a) State the dimensions of ρ.

   (b) Find the values of a, b and c for the model to be dimensionally consistent.

   (c) When the height of water in the tank has dropped to $\frac{1}{4}$ of its original value, what has happened to the speed of the water leaving the tank?   [A]

Key point summary

1 The dimensions of a quantity can be found by using   *p1*
either
- its definition, or
- a formula in which it is involved.

2 The notation [x] will be used to denote the dimensions   *p1*
of x, which will be given in terms of M, L and T.

3 The dimensions of a product are equal to the product   *p2*
of dimensions:

i.e. [ab] = [a] × [b].

4 $\left[\dfrac{dy}{dx}\right] = \dfrac{[y]}{[x]}$ *p3*

5 If [a] + [b] = [c] then a, b and c must all have the   *p4*
same dimensions.

6 Sin x, cos x and tan x are all dimensionless.   *p5*

7 The dimensions M, L and T are independent, so if it   *p7*
is known that

$$M^a L^b T^c = M^\alpha L^\beta T^\gamma$$

then for consistency, the following simultaneous
equations must hold,

$$a = \alpha, \quad b = \beta \quad \text{and} \quad c = \gamma.$$

Test yourself	**What to review**
1 The resistance force acting on a sphere of radius r and mass m, when it is moving at a speed v, has magnitude $mkrv$, where k is a constant. Determine the dimensions of k.	*Section 1.1*
2 The Universal Law of Gravitation states that the gravitational force exerted on a body of mass m by a body of mass M is $$\frac{GMm}{r^2}$$ where G is a constant and r is the distance between the centres of the two bodies. **(a)** Determine the dimensions of G in terms of M, L and T. **(b)** The speed, v, of a geostationary satellite orbiting a planet of mass m, is given by $$v = \frac{kG^x m^y}{r^z}$$ where r is the radius of the orbit, k is a dimensionless constant and x, y and z are constants. Determine the values of x, y and z for this equation to be dimensionally consistent.	*Section 1.2*

Test yourself ANSWERS

1 $L^{-1}T^{-1}$.

2 (a) $M^{-1}L^3T^{-2}$;   **(b)** $x = \frac{1}{2}$, $y = \frac{1}{2}$, $z = -\frac{1}{2}$.

CHAPTER 2
Relative velocity

Learning objectives

After studying this chapter you should be able to:
■ find the relative displacement and the distance between two particles in motion
■ find the velocity of one particle relative to another
■ choose the course a particle should follow to intercept another (if possible)
■ choose the course a particle should follow to approach another as closely as possible, if it cannot intercept it.

2.1 Introduction

Throughout this course in mechanics, acceleration, velocity, and displacement have all been analysed relative to a fixed origin, and in most examples only one particle has been involved. There are many situations in real life where two independent bodies are in motion; for example, ships at sea, or aircraft in flight. In this chapter we shall study the motion of a particle relative to another particle, which is itself in motion. We will investigate the position of one particle relative to the other, and how this varies according to the velocity of one relative to the other. This will enable us to find relative speeds, distances and times at which certain events occur.

2.2 Relative position

First we will investigate the relative displacement between two particles, which are in motion, and use this to find the distance between them.

Let A and B be two particles whose position vectors relative to an origin O are $\mathbf{r}_A$ and $\mathbf{r}_B$ respectively.

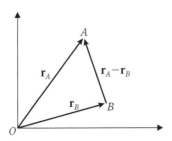

> The position of A relative to B is given by the vector $\mathbf{r}_A - \mathbf{r}_B$, which we shall denote by $\mathbf{r}_{AB}$. The distance between A and B is given by $|\mathbf{r}_{AB}| = |\mathbf{r}_A - \mathbf{r}_B|$.

Worked example 2.1

The position vectors of two particles, A and B, at time t relative to an origin O are

$$\mathbf{r}_A = (2t - 2)\mathbf{i} + (t + 1)\mathbf{j}$$

$$\mathbf{r}_B = t\mathbf{i} + 2\mathbf{j}$$

(where distance is in metres).

Find the distance between A and B at time t and hence find the shortest distance between A and B in the motion.

Solution

$$\mathbf{r}_A - \mathbf{r}_B = (t - 2)\mathbf{i} + (t - 1)\mathbf{j}$$

The distance between A and B is given by

$$r = |\mathbf{r}_A - \mathbf{r}_B| = \sqrt{(t - 2)^2 + (t - 1)^2} = \sqrt{2t^2 - 6t + 5}$$

To find the shortest distance between A and B we need to find the minimum value of r. There are two ways we can do this:

(a) we can use calculus, or

(b) we can complete the square in the quadratic in t.

In both methods, however, it is more convenient to find the minimum value of r^2.

(a) $r^2 = 2t^2 - 6t + 5$

$$\frac{d(r^2)}{dt} = 4t - 6 = 0 \text{ when } t = \tfrac{3}{2}$$

$$\frac{d^2(r^2)}{dt^2} = 4 > 0, \text{ so } r^2 \text{ has a minimum, when } t = \tfrac{3}{2}.$$

The minimum value of r^2 is $2 \times (\tfrac{3}{2})^2 + 2 \times (\tfrac{3}{2}) + 5 = \tfrac{1}{2}$.
Hence the minimum distance between A and B is $\sqrt{0.5} = 0.707$ m.

(b) Completing the square gives $r^2 = 2(t - \tfrac{3}{2})^2 + \tfrac{1}{2}$ which has a minimum value of $\tfrac{1}{2}$ when $t = \tfrac{3}{2}$. So the minimum distance between A and B is $\sqrt{0.5} = 0.707$ m.

Worked example 2.2

Particles A and B start at time $t = 0$ from points with position vectors $(10\mathbf{i} + 15\mathbf{j})$ m and $(5\mathbf{i} - 5\mathbf{j})$ m respectively, relative to a fixed origin O. The velocities of A and B are constant and equal to $(\mathbf{i} - \mathbf{j})$ m s^{-1} and $(2\mathbf{i} + 3\mathbf{j})$ m s^{-1} respectively. Show that the particles collide and find the value of t at which this occurs.

Solution

We are given $\mathbf{v}_A = (\mathbf{i} - \mathbf{j})$ which is constant for all t. We can integrate this to get the position vector of A.

$$\mathbf{r}_A = (\mathbf{i} - \mathbf{j})t + \mathbf{c}.$$

But when $t = 0$, $\mathbf{r}_A = (10\mathbf{i} + 15\mathbf{j}) \Rightarrow \mathbf{c} = (10\mathbf{i} + 15\mathbf{j})$

$$\mathbf{r}_A = (\mathbf{i} - \mathbf{j})t + (10\mathbf{i} + 15\mathbf{j}).$$

Similarly we can show that,

$$\mathbf{r}_B = (2\mathbf{i} + 3\mathbf{j})t + (5\mathbf{i} - 5\mathbf{j}).$$

The position vector of A relative to B is given by $\mathbf{r}_{AB} = \mathbf{r}_A - \mathbf{r}_B$,

$$\mathbf{r}_{AB} = (5 - t)\mathbf{i} + (20 - 4t)\mathbf{j}.$$

The particles will collide if both components of this vector become zero,

i.e. $5 - t = 0$ and $20 - 4t = 0$.

The value $t = 5$ satisfies both of these equations, therefore the particles do collide. If $t = 5$ is substituted into the expression for $\mathbf{r}_A$ and $\mathbf{r}_B$, then the coordinates of the point where the collision takes place can be found.

EXERCISE 2A

1 Particles A and B start at time $t = 0$ s from points with position vectors $(5\mathbf{i} - 13\mathbf{j})$ m and $(2\mathbf{i} - \mathbf{j})$ m respectively, relative to a fixed origin. The velocities of A and B are constant and equal to $(2\mathbf{i} - \mathbf{j})$ m s^{-1} and $(3\mathbf{i} - 5\mathbf{j})$ m s^{-1} respectively. Show that the particles collide and find the value of t at which this occurs.

2 Particles A and B start at time $t = 0$ s from points with position vectors $(5\mathbf{i} + 13\mathbf{j})$ m and $(7\mathbf{i} + 5\mathbf{j})$ m respectively, relative to a fixed origin. The velocities of A and B are constant and equal to $(3\mathbf{i} - 5\mathbf{j})$ m s^{-1} and $(2\mathbf{i} - \mathbf{j})$ m s^{-1} respectively.

   (a) Show that the particles collide and find the position vector of the point of intersection.

   (b) Determine the angle between the directions of motion of A and B before collision. [A]

3 Initially, a cyclist, A, passes through a point with position vector $(-9\mathbf{i} - 5\mathbf{j})$ km relative to an origin O and is travelling with a constant velocity of $(9\mathbf{i} + 7\mathbf{j})$ km h^{-1}. At the same instant another cyclist, B, leaves O travelling with a constant velocity $(5.4\mathbf{i} + 5\mathbf{j})$ km h^{-1}.

(a) Write down the position vector of *A* at time *t* hours.

(b) Write down the position vector of *B* at time *t* hours.

(c) Find the time when the two cyclists have the same position.

4 At time $t = 0$, a ship, *A*, is 8 km due west of a ship, *B*. To an observer on ship *B*, ship *A* is moving with constant velocity $(3\mathbf{i} - 4\mathbf{j})$ m s^{-1}, where $\mathbf{i}$ and $\mathbf{j}$ are unit vectors directed east and north respectively.

(a) Find the position vector of ship *A* relative to ship *B* at time *t* s.

(b) Show that the ships are closest together after 16 minutes and find the distance apart at this time.

(c) The visibility is such that ship *A* will sight ship *B* when the ships are less than 7 km apart. Find the times between which sightings will occur. [A]

5 Two long straight roads intersect at right angles at a crossroads, *O*. Two vehicles, one on each road, travel with constant speeds of 25 m s^{-1} and 20 m s^{-1} respectively. At time $t = 0$ they are both a distance of 610 m from *O* and are approaching *O*. Write down their respective distances from *O* at time *t* s and find the value of *t* when the vehicles are closest together. [A]

6 A car and a cyclist are travelling with constant velocities $\mathbf{v}_1$ m s^{-1} and $\mathbf{v}_2$ m s^{-1} respectively, where $\mathbf{v}_1 = 9\mathbf{i} + 3\sqrt{3}\mathbf{j}$, and $\mathbf{v}_2 = 2\mathbf{i} + 2\sqrt{3}\mathbf{j}$ and $\mathbf{i}$ and $\mathbf{j}$ are unit vectors pointing due east and due north respectively. At time $t = 0$ the cyclist is 52 m due east of the car. Find the position vector of the cyclist relative to the car at time *t* s. Hence find the least distance between the car and the cyclist and the time at which this occurs. [A]

7 A car, *A*, is travelling with a constant velocity of 20 km h^{-1} due west and a cyclist, *B*, has a constant velocity of 16 km h^{-1} in the direction of the vector $(-4\mathbf{i} + 3\mathbf{j})$, where $\mathbf{i}$ and $\mathbf{j}$ are unit vectors due east and due north respectively. At noon *A* is 1.2 km due north of *B*. Take the position of *A* at noon as the origin and obtain expressions for the position vectors of *A* and *B* at time *t* hours after noon, and hence show that the position vector of *A* relative to *B* is $\mathbf{r}$ km, where

$$5\mathbf{r} = 6[-6t\mathbf{i} + (1 - 8t)\mathbf{j}].$$

Deduce that the distance between *A* and *B* is *d* km, where

$$25d^2 = 36(100t^2 - 16t + 1).$$

Hence show that the minimum separation between *A* and *B* is 720 m and find the time at which this occurs. [A]

2.3 Relative velocity

In this section we investigate the relationship between the velocities of two particles, and the velocity of one particle relative to the other.

The position vector of A relative to B is $\mathbf{r}_{AB}$, and the velocity of A relative to B is denoted by $\mathbf{v}_{AB}$.

> If the velocity of A is $\mathbf{v}_A$ and the velocity of B is $\mathbf{v}_B$, then the velocity of A relative to B, $\mathbf{v}_{AB}$, is given by
>
> $$\mathbf{v}_{AB} = \mathbf{v}_A - \mathbf{v}_B.$$

The equation $\mathbf{v}_{AB} = \mathbf{v}_A - \mathbf{v}_B$ can be rearranged to give,

> $$\mathbf{v}_A = \mathbf{v}_{AB} + \mathbf{v}_B$$

This gives the velocity of A as the sum of the velocity of B plus the velocity of A relative to B.

In general these results can be used in three dimensions, involving the unit vectors $\mathbf{i}$, $\mathbf{j}$, and $\mathbf{k}$. However, most applications involve constant velocities and two dimensions.

Worked example 2.3

The velocity of a ship, B, is $(10\mathbf{i} + 10\mathbf{j})$ km h^{-1}, where the unit vectors $\mathbf{i}$ and $\mathbf{j}$ are directed to the east and north respectively. From ship B, a second ship, A, appears to be sailing at 20 km h^{-1} on a bearing of 330°. Find the velocity of A.

Solution

In this question we are given $\mathbf{v}_B = 10\mathbf{i} + 10\mathbf{j}$

and $\mathbf{v}_{AB} = -20 \sin 30° \, \mathbf{i} + 20 \cos 30° \, \mathbf{j}$.

Rearranging $\mathbf{v}_{AB} = \mathbf{v}_A - \mathbf{v}_B$ we get $\mathbf{v}_A = \mathbf{v}_{AB} + \mathbf{v}_B$

$$\mathbf{v}_A = -20 \sin 30° \, \mathbf{i} + 20 \cos 30° \, \mathbf{j} + 10\mathbf{i} + 10\mathbf{j}$$
$$= 10(1 + \sqrt{3})\mathbf{j} \text{ km h}^{-1}$$

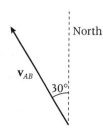

Worked example 2.4

A particle, A, is travelling northeast with speed v_A m s^{-1} and a particle, B, is travelling southeast with speed v_B m s^{-1}. The velocity of A relative to B is $(10\mathbf{i} + 14\mathbf{j})$ m s^{-1}, where $\mathbf{i}$ and $\mathbf{j}$ are unit vectors directed east and north respectively. Find v_A and v_B.

Solution

The velocity of A is parallel to $(\mathbf{i} + \mathbf{j}) \Rightarrow \mathbf{v}_A = \lambda(\mathbf{i} + \mathbf{j})$.
The velocity of B is parallel to $(\mathbf{i} - \mathbf{j}) \Rightarrow \mathbf{v}_B = \mu(\mathbf{i} - \mathbf{j})$.
Where λ and μ are constants to be found.

Using $\mathbf{v}_{AB} = \mathbf{v}_A - \mathbf{v}_B$, we have

$$10\mathbf{i} + 14\mathbf{j} = \lambda(\mathbf{i} + \mathbf{j}) - \mu(\mathbf{i} - \mathbf{j})$$

$$10\mathbf{i} + 14\mathbf{j} = (\lambda - \mu)\mathbf{i} + (\lambda + \mu)\mathbf{j}$$

By equating coefficients of $\mathbf{i}$ and $\mathbf{j}$, from both sides of this equation, we obtain a pair of simultaneous equations for λ and μ.

$$10 = \lambda - \mu$$

$$14 = \lambda + \mu$$

The solution of these equations is $\lambda = 12$ and $\mu = 2$.

Hence $\mathbf{v}_A = \lambda(\mathbf{i} + \mathbf{j}) = 12(\mathbf{i} + \mathbf{j}) \Rightarrow v_A = 12\sqrt{2} \text{ m s}^{-1}$,

and $\mathbf{v}_B = \mu(\mathbf{i} - \mathbf{j}) = 2(\mathbf{i} - \mathbf{j}) \Rightarrow v_B = 2\sqrt{2} \text{ m s}^{-1}$.

Worked example 2.5 _____

The velocity of a particle, B, is $(5\mathbf{i} + 12\mathbf{j}) \text{ m s}^{-1}$. The velocity of a particle, A, relative to B is parallel to $(\mathbf{i} + \mathbf{j})$. A third particle, C, has velocity $(3\mathbf{i} + 4\mathbf{j}) \text{ m s}^{-1}$, and the velocity of A relative to C is parallel to $(\mathbf{i} + 2\mathbf{j})$. Find the velocity of A.

Solution

$$\mathbf{v}_{AB} = \mathbf{v}_A - \mathbf{v}_B \qquad \text{and} \qquad \mathbf{v}_{AC} = \mathbf{v}_A - \mathbf{v}_C$$

$$\lambda(\mathbf{i} + \mathbf{j}) = \mathbf{v}_A - (5\mathbf{i} + 12\mathbf{j}) \qquad \mu(\mathbf{i} + 2\mathbf{j}) = \mathbf{v}_A - (3\mathbf{i} + 4\mathbf{j})$$

$$\mathbf{v}_A = (5 + \lambda)\mathbf{i} + (12 + \lambda)\mathbf{j} \qquad \mathbf{v}_A = (3 + \mu)\mathbf{i} + (4 + 2\mu)\mathbf{j}$$

These two equations for $\mathbf{v}_A$ gives two simultaneous equations for λ and μ.

$$5 + \lambda = 3 + \mu$$

and $\quad 12 + \lambda = 4 + 2\mu$

The solution of these equations is $\lambda = 4$, and $\mu = 6$. Using either of these gives,

$$\mathbf{v}_A = 9\mathbf{i} + 16\mathbf{j}.$$

Geometrical approach

The vector relationship $\mathbf{v}_{AB} = \mathbf{v}_A - \mathbf{v}_B$ has a simple representation as a triangle of vectors.

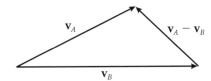

The sine and cosine rules can be used in this triangle to find velocities.

Worked example 2.6

A yacht, A, is sailing east at $5\ \text{km h}^{-1}$. A second yacht, B, is sailing on a bearing of $330°$ at a speed of $5\ \text{km h}^{-1}$. Find the magnitude and direction of the velocity of A relative to B.

Solution

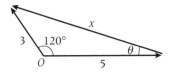

Using the cosine rule in the above triangle,

$$x^2 = 5^2 + 3^2 - 2 \times 5 \times 3 \times \cos 120° = 49 \Rightarrow x = 7$$

Using the sine rule we can now find θ,

$$\frac{\sin \theta}{3} = \frac{\sin 120°}{7} \Rightarrow \theta = 22°$$

Hence the velocity of A relative to B is $7\ \text{km h}^{-1}$ on a bearing of $292°$.

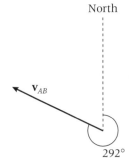

Worked example 2.7

To a man walking due east at $4\ \text{km h}^{-1}$ the wind appears to be blowing from the northeast at $10\ \text{km h}^{-1}$. Find the velocity of the wind.

Solution

In this example we know the velocity of the man, $\mathbf{v}_m$, and the velocity of the wind relative to the man $\mathbf{v}_{wm}$. We now add these velocities to find the velocity of the wind, $\mathbf{v}_w$.

$$\mathbf{v}_w = \mathbf{v}_{wm} + \mathbf{v}_m$$

From the cosine rule in the above triangle,

$$x^2 = 10^2 + 4^2 - 2 \times 10 \times 4 \times \cos 45° \Rightarrow x = 7.71$$

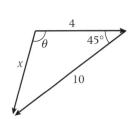

From the sine rule,

$$\frac{\sin \theta}{10} = \frac{\sin 45°}{x} \Rightarrow \theta = 113°$$

The wind is blowing at 7.71 km h⁻¹ *from* the direction N23°E.

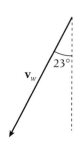

Worked example 2.8

Two airports, A and B, are 1000 km apart with A being due west of B. An aeroplane, P, flies directly from A to B, and is capable of flying at 300 km h⁻¹ in still air. The wind blows from the southwest at 50 km h⁻¹. Find the bearing which the pilot follows, the speed of the aircraft relative to the earth, and the length of the flight.

Solution

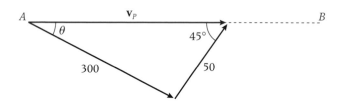

The question gives us the velocity of the wind, $\mathbf{v}_W$, and the velocity of the aircraft relative to the wind, $\mathbf{v}_{PW}$. We are also told that the actual velocity of the aircraft, $\mathbf{v}_P$, is towards the east. The problem can be solved either by using vector methods or by using trigonometry in the above triangle.

From the sine rule,

$$\frac{\sin \theta}{50} = \frac{\sin 45°}{300} \Rightarrow \theta = 6.77°$$

The bearing which the pilot follows is 097°, to the nearest degree. Considering easterly components of velocity in the above triangle,

$$|\mathbf{v}_P| = 300 \cos \theta + 50 \cos 45° = 333 \text{ km h}^{-1}$$

The length of the flight will be $1000 \div 333 = 3$ hours.

EXERCISE 2B

1 A jet is approaching an airport with velocity
$(300\mathbf{i} + 400\mathbf{j})$ km h⁻¹. A passenger on the jet sees a helicopter in the distance whose velocity is $(50\mathbf{i} - 150\mathbf{j} + 10\mathbf{k})$ km h⁻¹.

   (a) What is the velocity of the helicopter relative to the jet?

   (b) What is the velocity of the jet relative to the helicopter?

2 The velocity of A is $(3\mathbf{i} + 2\mathbf{j})$ km h^{-1} and the velocity of B is $(5\mathbf{i} - 3\mathbf{j})$ km h^{-1}. If $\mathbf{i}$ and $\mathbf{j}$ are unit vectors directed east and north respectively, find the bearing of the velocity of A relative to B.

3 To a cyclist riding with velocity $(15\mathbf{i} + 15\mathbf{j})$ km h^{-1} a steady wind appears to have velocity $(3\mathbf{i} - 5\mathbf{j})$ km h^{-1}. What is the actual velocity of the wind?

4 The velocity of a ship, A, relative to another ship, B, is $(4\mathbf{i} + 3\mathbf{j})$ km h^{-1}. Relative to a stationary observer, O, the ship A is travelling with constant speed in the direction of $(\mathbf{i} + \mathbf{j})$ and the ship B is also travelling with constant speed but in the direction of $(2\mathbf{i} + 3\mathbf{j})$. Find the velocities of A and B.

5 The velocity of a ship, A, relative to another ship, B, is $(10\mathbf{i} + 24\mathbf{j})$ km h^{-1}. Relative to a stationary observer, O, the ship A is travelling with constant speed in the direction of $(2\mathbf{i} + 3\mathbf{j})$ and the ship B is also travelling with constant speed but in the direction of $(\mathbf{i} - \mathbf{j})$. Find the velocities of A and B relative to O.

6 A cyclist, A, is travelling east at 20 km h^{-1}. A second cyclist, B, is travelling on a bearing of 120° at a speed of 15 km h^{-1}. Find the magnitude and bearing of the velocity of A relative to B.

7 Two particles, A and B, have speeds 20 m s^{-1} and 30 m s^{-1} respectively, relative to a fixed origin O. If the angle between the velocities of A and B is 20°, find the speed of A relative to B.

8 Two particles, A and B, have speeds 25 m s^{-1} and 10 m s^{-1} respectively, relative to a fixed origin O. The speed of A relative to B is 20 m s^{-1}, find the angle between the velocities of A and B.

9 A particle, B, has a speed of 20 m s^{-1} relative to an origin O. A second particle, A, has a speed of 30 m s^{-1}, relative to B. If the angle between the velocity of B and the velocity of A relative to B is 120°, find the speed of A relative to O.

10 If A is travelling north, B is travelling southeast, and if A appears to be travelling on a bearing of 345° relative to B, find the ratio of the speed of A to the speed of B.

11 Relative to an origin O, particle A is travelling in the direction of $(3\mathbf{i} + 4\mathbf{j})$, and particle B is travelling in the direction of $(5\mathbf{i} + 12\mathbf{j})$. The velocity of A relative to B is in the direction of $(\mathbf{i} + \mathbf{j})$. Find the ratio of the speeds of A and B.

12 Two airfields, *A* and *B*, are 2000 km apart with *A* due west of *B*. An aircraft, *P*, flies directly from *A* to *B*, and is capable of flying at 500 km h^{-1} in still air. The wind blows from the north at 50 km h^{-1}. Find the bearing that the pilot must set to fly straight to *B*, the speed of the aircraft relative to the earth, and the time of the flight.

13 The diagram shows two points, *A* and *B*, which are on opposite sides of a river, and are 100 m apart. A boat, *P*, is rowed so that it moves directly from *A* to *B*, and would travel at 4 m s^{-1} in still water. There is a constant current of 2 m s^{-1}. Find the course, which the oarsman must follow, and how long the journey takes.

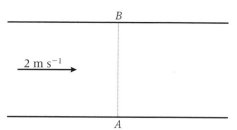

14 A boat travels at 4 m s^{-1} in still water. A river is 100 m wide and the current flows at 2 m s^{-1}. Find the shortest time possible to cross the river, and the distance downstream that the boat is carried.

15 A river with long straight banks is 500 m wide and flows with a constant speed of 3 m s^{-1}. A man rowing a boat at a steady speed of 5 m s^{-1}, relative to the river, sets off from a point, *A*, on one bank so as to arrive at the point, *B*, directly opposite *A* on the other bank. Find the time taken to cross the river. A woman also sets off at *A* rowing at 5 m s^{-1} relative to the river and crosses in the shortest possible time. Find this time and the distance downstream of *B* of the point at which she lands. [A]

16 A river flows at 6 m s^{-1} between parallel banks which are 40 m apart. A man rows his boat at a speed of 5 m s^{-1} so as to cross the river, reaching the far bank 30 m downstream of the starting point. Find the two possible values of the angle between his course and the bank.

17 A river flows at 5 m s^{-1} from west to east between parallel banks which are at a distance 300 m apart. A man rows a boat at a speed of 3 m s^{-1} in still water.
  (a) State the direction in which the boat must be steered in order to cross the river from the southern bank to the northern bank in the shortest possible time. Find the time taken and the actual distance covered by the boat for this crossing.
  (b) Find the direction in which the boat must be steered in order to cross the river from the southern bank to the northern bank by the shortest possible route. Find the time taken and the actual distance covered by the boat for this crossing.

2

18 Two airports, A and B, are 1000 km apart with A northeast of B. A jet flies with a constant airspeed of 300 km h^{-1} directly from A to B and back. Throughout the whole journey there is a constant wind of 50 km h^{-1} from the north. Find the average speed of the jet for the whole trip.

19 An old man cycles to work each day leaving his home at a point with position vector $(-2\mathbf{i} - 8\mathbf{j})$ km relative to an origin O at the centre of the village. The unit vectors $\mathbf{i}$ and $\mathbf{j}$ point east and north respectively. One day he cycles due north at 8 km h^{-1}. At the same time, a younger man leaves his home, which has position vector $(-12\mathbf{i} - 4\mathbf{j})$ km relative to O, and cycles with velocity $(6\mathbf{i} - 6\mathbf{j})$ km h^{-1}. Show that after half an hour the cyclists are closest together and determine the closest distance between them. On that day as the men cycle to work there is a steady wind blowing. To the older man cycling due north at 8 km h^{-1}, the wind appears to be blowing from the west. To the younger man, cycling with velocity $(6\mathbf{i} - 6\mathbf{j})$ km h^{-1}, the wind appears to be blowing from the south. Find the velocity of the wind as a vector. [A]

20 The velocity of a particle, B, is $(-2\mathbf{i} + 5\mathbf{j})$ m s^{-1}. The velocity of a particle, A, relative to B is parallel to $(3\mathbf{i} + \mathbf{j})$. A third particle, C, has velocity $(-\mathbf{i} - 3\mathbf{j})$ m s^{-1}, and the velocity of A relative to C is parallel to $(\mathbf{i} + 2\mathbf{j})$. Find the velocity of A.

21 A particle B is travelling northeast with speed $2\sqrt{2}$ km h^{-1}. A second particle C is travelling south with speed 2 km h^{-1}. A third particle A is travelling east relative to B, and is travelling northeast relative to C. Let $\mathbf{i}$ and $\mathbf{j}$ be unit vectors in the directions east and north respectively. Write down the velocities of B and C in terms of $\mathbf{i}$ and $\mathbf{j}$, and hence find the velocity of A.

22 Two cyclists, A and B, travel along a level straight road. A travels north at 10 mph and B travels south also at 10 mph. They both spot a hawk in flight. Relative to A, the hawk appears to be flying on a bearing of 057°, whereas relative to B it appears to be flying on a bearing of 033°. Find the velocity of the hawk relative to the ground, correct to 2 significant figures and in terms of the unit vectors $\mathbf{i}$ and $\mathbf{j}$ which are directed east and north respectively.

23 Axes Ox, Oy, and Oz are defined respectively in the north, west and vertically upwards directions. Unit vectors $\mathbf{i}$, $\mathbf{j}$ and $\mathbf{k}$ are defined in the x, y and z directions. At noon two aeroplanes, A and B, take off from different airports. At time 1215, the velocity of A is $300\mathbf{i} + 200\mathbf{j}$ miles per hour, and the velocity of B is $-150\mathbf{i} + 350\mathbf{j} + 0.1\mathbf{k}$ miles per hour. Assume that these velocities are constant over the next 12 minutes.

(a) Find the velocity of B relative to A during these next 12 minutes.

(b) Time t is measured in hours after 1215. At 1215, the position of B relative to A is $50\mathbf{i} + 10\mathbf{j} + 0.4\mathbf{k}$ miles. Find the position vector of B relative to A when $t = 0.1$.

(c) Find an expression for the distance in miles which the aeroplanes are apart at time t, where $0 < t < 0.2$.

(d) Hence find the time at which the aeroplanes are nearest to each other, and the shortest distance apart. [A]

24 A cyclist travels north along a straight level road at a speed of u m s^{-1}, and, relative to the cyclist, the wind appears to be blowing from the southwest. Further along his journey the cyclist turns through $\theta°$ to the right $(0 < \theta < 90°)$ into a side road, and so the cyclist now travels on a bearing of $\theta°$ and at the same speed. On the new bearing the wind now appears to be blowing from the southeast. Show that the speed of the wind, relative to the ground, v, satisfies the equation,

$$v^2 = u^2(1 + \sin\theta\cos\theta).$$

2.4 Interception

In this section we will consider two particles, A and B, which have known positions at a certain point in time, and where particle B moves with a given constant velocity. Here we chose the course that the particle A must take if it is to intercept B.

If the velocities of the two particles, $\mathbf{v}_A$ and $\mathbf{v}_B$, are constant, then

$$\mathbf{r}_A = \mathbf{v}_A t + \mathbf{r}_{A0} \qquad (1)$$

where $\mathbf{r}_{A0}$ is the position vector of A and when $t = 0$.

Similarly,

$$\mathbf{r}_B = \mathbf{v}_B t + \mathbf{r}_{B0} \qquad (2)$$

where $\mathbf{r}_{B0}$ is the position vector of B when $t = 0$.

The particles will intercept each other when,

$$\mathbf{r}_A = \mathbf{r}_B.$$

Using equations (1) and (2) we get,

$$\mathbf{v}_A t + \mathbf{r}_{A0} = \mathbf{v}_B t + \mathbf{r}_{B0}$$

$$(\mathbf{v}_A - \mathbf{v}_B)t = \mathbf{r}_{B0} - \mathbf{r}_{A0}$$

The equation

$$(\mathbf{v}_A - \mathbf{v}_B)t = \mathbf{r}_{B0} - \mathbf{r}_{A0}$$

implies that if A is to intercept B then the velocity of A relative to B must be parallel to the initial displacement $\overrightarrow{A_0B_0}$. The following diagram shows this relationship.

Here we consider the particle B to be at rest. The velocity of A relative to B can be thought to be the sum of two separate velocities $\mathbf{v}_A$ and $-\mathbf{v}_B$. The velocity $-\mathbf{v}_B$ is known and the velocity $\mathbf{v}_A$ is found so that $\mathbf{v}_{AB}$ is towards B.

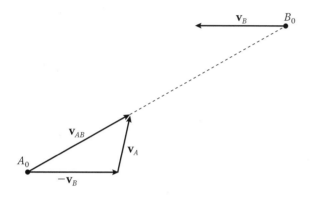

The above equation can also be used to find the time, t, that A will take to intercept B.

$$t = \frac{|\mathbf{r}_{B0} - \mathbf{r}_{A0}|}{|\mathbf{v}_{AB}|}$$

Worked example 2.9

A ship, A, is to intercept a second ship, B, which is 100 km away on a bearing if 030°. B is sailing on a course of 330° at 20 km h^{-1}. If the speed of A is 40 km h^{-1}, find the course that A must steer, to the nearest degree, and also the time taken for A to reach B.

Solution

The left-hand diagram shows the initial position of A (A_0) and B (B_0). At B_0 the velocity of B ($\mathbf{v}_B$) has been drawn. At A_0 the vector $-\mathbf{v}_B$ has been drawn. The velocity of A ($\mathbf{v}_A$) has been placed on the end of this vector so that the velocity of A relative to B acts towards B_0.

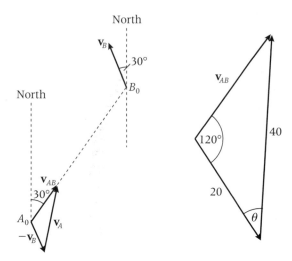

The diagram on the right shows the velocity triangle from which we can find $v_{AB} = |\mathbf{v}_{AB}|$ and θ.

Using the cosine rule in the velocity diagram,

$$1600 = 400 + v_{AB}^2 - 40\,v_{AB}\cos 120°$$
$$v_{AB}^2 + 20\,v_{AB} - 1200 = 0$$
$$v_{AB} = 26.1 \text{ km h}^{-1}.$$

From the sine rule,

$$\frac{\sin\theta}{v_{AB}} = \frac{\sin 120°}{40}$$
$$\theta = 34.3°$$

The course that A must steer is therefore $\theta - 30 = 004°$ to the nearest degree.

The time that A will take to intercept B will be

$$\frac{100}{26.1} = 3.84 \text{ hours} = 3 \text{ hours and } 50 \text{ minutes.}$$

Worked example 2.10

A man is southeast of a cyclist. If the cyclist is heading east at 20 km h^{-1}, find the minimum speed with which the man must run if he is to intercept the cyclist.

Solution

In this question we need to determine the direction of the vector $\mathbf{v}_M$, so that its length is a minimum. This occurs when $\mathbf{v}_M$ is perpendicular to the direction of $\mathbf{v}_{MC}$, (which is fixed). Hence the minimum speed of the man is

$$20 \sin 45° = 14.1 \text{ km h}^{-1}.$$

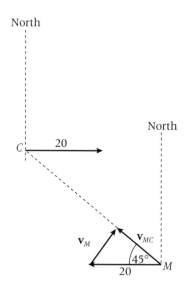

Worked example 2.11

Two particles, A and B, have position vectors $(31\mathbf{i} + 31\mathbf{j})$ m and $(17\mathbf{i} - 11\mathbf{j})$ m, respectively, when $t = 0$. Particle B has a constant velocity of $(-\mathbf{i} + 2\mathbf{j})$ m s^{-1}. The speed of A is 5 m s^{-1} and later intercepts B. Find the velocity of A, and when the interception occurs.

Solution

$$\mathbf{v}_B = -\mathbf{i} + 2\mathbf{j}$$
$$\mathbf{r}_B = (-\mathbf{i} + 2\mathbf{j}) + \mathbf{c}$$

But when $t = 0$, $\mathbf{r}_B = (17\mathbf{i} - 11\mathbf{j}) \Rightarrow \mathbf{c} = (17\mathbf{i} - 11\mathbf{j})$, hence

$$\mathbf{r}_B = (-\mathbf{i} + 2\mathbf{j})t + (17\mathbf{i} - 11\mathbf{j})$$
$$= (17 - t)\mathbf{i} + (2t - 11)\mathbf{j}.$$

Letting $\mathbf{v}_A = p\mathbf{i} + q\mathbf{j}$, and using the same approach as above we can show that,

$$\mathbf{r}_A = (31 + pt)\mathbf{i} + (31 + qt)\mathbf{j}.$$

The two particles intersect where $\mathbf{r}_A = \mathbf{r}_B$

i.e. $\quad (31 + pt)\mathbf{i} + (31 + qt)\mathbf{j} = (17 - t)\mathbf{i} + (2t - 11)\mathbf{j}$

equating coefficients of $\mathbf{i}$ and $\mathbf{j}$,

$$31 + pt = 17 - t \;\Rightarrow t(p + 1) = -14$$
$$31 + qt = 2t - 11 \Rightarrow t(q - 2) = -42.$$

Eliminating t from these equations we get,

$$q = 3p + 5. \tag{1}$$

But we know that the speed of A is 5, so

$$p^2 + q^2 = 25. \tag{2}$$

Substituting for q from (1) into (2) leads to

$$10p^2 + 30p = 0 \Rightarrow p = 0, \text{ or } p = -3.$$

However, if $p = 0$, we get $t = -14$, which is not a later time, if $p = -3$ we get $t = 7$, which is the required solution.

Finally, the velocity of A is $-3\mathbf{i} - 4\mathbf{j}$, and interception occurs after 7 s.

EXERCISE 2C

1 A helicopter leaves a port to intercept a ship as soon as possible. When the helicopter leaves the port the ship is 100 km due north of the port. The ship maintains a constant speed of 30 km h^{-1} due east and the speed of the helicopter is 80 km h^{-1}. Find the bearing of the course which the helicopter should follow to intercept the ship and the time the journey will take.

2 A battleship sails to intercept a destroyer which is on a bearing of 130°. The battleship maintains a steady speed of 50 km h^{-1} on a course of 160°. If the speed of the destroyer is 30 km h^{-1} and the journey takes $2\frac{1}{2}$ hours, find the possible initial distances between the two ships.

3 Two joggers, A and B, each run at 10 km h^{-1}. Initially B is on a bearing of 120° from A and running north. What direction should A run to intercept B?

4 Two similar frigates, P and Q, each sail with speed 20 km h^{-1}. Initially Q is 100 km from P on a bearing of 320° and is on a course of 200°.

   (a) What is the bearing of the course that P takes to intercept Q, and how long does the journey take?

   (b) If the speed of P were 19 km h^{-1} instead, what would be the two possible courses that P could take?

5 Let $\mathbf{i}$ and $\mathbf{j}$ be unit vectors, directed east and north respectively. A windsurfer on a damaged board is drifting in the sea with velocity $5\mathbf{j}$ km h^{-1}. A coastal rescue helicopter, travelling at its maximum speed of 100 km h^{-1}, moves to rescue the windsurfer in the shortest possible time. Initially the windsurfer has position vector $-20\mathbf{i}$ km relative to the helicopter. Let $(u\mathbf{i} + v\mathbf{j})$ km h^{-1} be the velocity of the helicopter.

   (a) Find the position vectors of the windsurfer and the helicopter at time t hours relative to the initial position of the helicopter.

   (b) Calculate the time, in minutes, for the helicopter to reach the windsurfer and the bearing of the course, to the nearest degree, taken by the helicopter. [A]

6 Two particles, A and B, initially have position vectors $(-930\mathbf{i} + 390\mathbf{j})$ m and $(-210\mathbf{i} - 330\mathbf{j})$ m, respectively. Particle B has a constant velocity of $(3\mathbf{i} + 4\mathbf{j})$ m s^{-1}. The speed of A is 13 m s^{-1}. At time t s A intercepts B. Find the velocity of A, the coordinates of the point of interception, and the value of t when the interception occurs.

7 Two particles, A and B, have position vectors $(10\mathbf{i} + 15\mathbf{j})$ m and $(5\mathbf{i} - 5\mathbf{j})$ m, respectively, when $t = 0$. Particle B has a constant velocity of $(2\mathbf{i} + 3\mathbf{j})$ m s^{-1}. The speed of A is $\sqrt{2}$ m s^{-1} and later intercepts B. Find the two possible velocities of A, the corresponding coordinates of the point of interception, and the corresponding values of t when the interception occurs.

8 The initial position vector $(t = 0)$ of a boat, B, relative to a second boat, A, is $(50\mathbf{i} + 325\mathbf{j})$ m. The velocity of B is $(4\mathbf{i} - 5\mathbf{j})$ m s^{-1}, and the velocity of A is parallel to $(3\mathbf{i} + 4\mathbf{j})$.

Given that the two boats collide, find the velocity of A, the value of t when collision occurs, and the position vector relative to A of the point where collision occurs.

9 Two boats, A and B, have velocities $(2\mathbf{i} + 5\mathbf{j})$ m s^{-1} and $(-8\mathbf{i} + 10\mathbf{j})$ m s^{-1} respectively, where $\mathbf{i}$ and $\mathbf{j}$ are unit vectors directed east and north respectively. Given that at noon, A is 100 km west, and h km north of B and that the boats are on collision course, find h.

10 The velocities of two boats, A and B, are given to be $(3\mathbf{i} + 4\mathbf{j})$ m s^{-1} and $(5.5\mathbf{i} + 2\mathbf{j})$ m s^{-1} respectively, where $\mathbf{i}$ and $\mathbf{j}$ are unit vectors directed east and north respectively.
  (a) Express in the form $(a\mathbf{i} + b\mathbf{j})$ the velocity of B relative to A.
  Given that at noon, B is 9 km west, and h km north of A and that the boats are on collision course find:
  (b) the value of h,
  (c) the time at which the collision occurs.   [A]

2.5 Closest approach

Consider two particles, A and B, which move with constant velocities $\mathbf{v}_A$ and $\mathbf{v}_B$, such that when $t = 0$ the position vectors of A and B are $\mathbf{r}_{A0}$ and $\mathbf{r}_{B0}$ respectively. Equations (1) and (2) from the previous section give,

$$\mathbf{r}_A = \mathbf{v}_A t + \mathbf{r}_{A0} \text{ and}$$
$$\mathbf{r}_B = \mathbf{v}_B t + \mathbf{r}_{B0}.$$

Subtracting these vectors gives,

$$\mathbf{r}_A - \mathbf{r}_B = (\mathbf{r}_{A0} - \mathbf{r}_{B0}) + t(\mathbf{v}_A - \mathbf{v}_B)$$
$$\mathbf{r}_{AB} = (\mathbf{r}_{A0} - \mathbf{r}_{B0}) + t\mathbf{v}_{AB} \tag{3}$$

The following diagram shows the general motion of A relative to B.

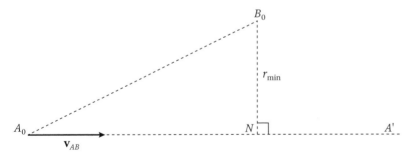

Relative to B, A will move along the line A_0A'. The particles will be closest together when A is at N. We can find this minimum distance using vector methods (the method used in section 1 of this chapter), or we can use a more geometrical approach and draw a diagram, as above. The next worked example demonstrates the geometrical approach.

Worked example 2.12

Two ships, A and B, have velocities of $20 \, \text{km h}^{-1}$ and $25 \, \text{km h}^{-1}$ on bearings of $210°$ and $100°$ respectively. At noon A is 100 km east of B. Find the closest distance between the ships in the ensuing motion and the time that they are closest, assuming that their velocities remain constant.

Solution

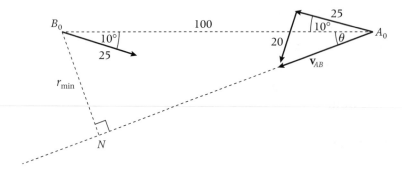

The above diagram shows the initial position of A (A_0) and B (B_0). At B_0 the velocity of B ($\mathbf{v}_B$) has been drawn. At A_0 the vector $-\mathbf{v}_B$ has been drawn. The velocity of A ($\mathbf{v}_A$) has been placed on the end of this vector. The velocity of A relative to B is the resultant of these two vectors, as shown.

The minimum distance between the ships is $100 \sin \theta$. The angle θ can be found by using the sine and cosine rules in the velocity triangle.

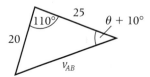

From the cosine rule,

$$v_{AB}^2 = 20^2 + 25^2 - 2 \times 20 \times 25 \times \cos 110°$$
$$v_{AB} = 37.0 \, \text{km h}^{-1}.$$

From the sine rule,

$$\frac{\sin (\theta + 10°)}{20} = \frac{\sin 110 \, \theta}{v_{AB}}$$
$$\theta = 20.6°.$$

The closest distance between the ships $100 \sin \theta = 35.1$ km.

The time taken to arrive at this point is given by,

$$\frac{A_0 N}{v_{AB}} = \frac{100 \cos 20.6°}{37.0} = 2.53 \text{ hours, which is at 14:32.}$$

Course for closest approach

Let particles A and B move with constant velocities $\mathbf{v}_A$ and $\mathbf{v}_B$, respectively, and have positions A_0 and B_0, respectively, when $t = 0$.

In a previous section we considered the course that particle A must follow if it is to intercept B. We chose the velocity of A so that $\mathbf{v}_{AB}$ is parallel to $\overrightarrow{A_0B_0}$ as in the diagram below.

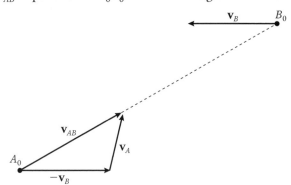

However, it is not always possible to achieve this. Sometimes the maximum speed of A is less than the speed of B. In this case we may be asked to determine the course which A should choose if it is to approach as near as possible to B.

 The following diagram shows that if $\mathbf{v}_A$ is perpendicular to $\mathbf{v}_{AB}$, then A approaches B as closely as possible.

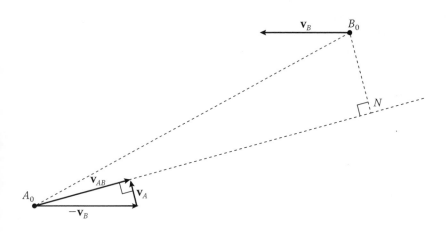

 The minimum distance between the particles is given by B_0N.

 The time taken for A to reach the closest point is given by
$$t = \frac{A_0N}{\mathbf{v}_{AB}}$$

Worked example 2.13

Two ships, A and B, are 100 km apart, with A due west of B. Ship B is travelling at 30 km h^{-1} on a bearing of 220°. The maximum speed of A is 15 km h^{-1}. Find the course that A should take if it is to approach B as closely as possible, and find the shortest distance between the ships.

Solution

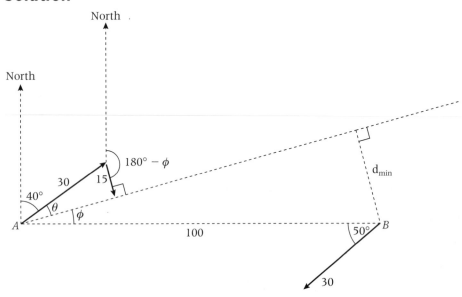

The above diagram shows the initial positions of A (A_0) and B (B_0). At B_0 the velocity of B ($\mathbf{v}_B$) has been drawn. At A_0 the vector $-\mathbf{v}_B$ has been drawn. The velocity of A ($\mathbf{v}_A$) has been placed on the end of this vector so that it is perpendicular to the resultant of $-\mathbf{v}_B$ and $\mathbf{v}_A$ (which is, of course, the velocity of A relative to B).

From the triangle of velocities we can find θ,

$$\sin \theta = \frac{15}{30} = 0.5 \Rightarrow \theta = 30°.$$

This gives, $\phi = 50 - 30 = 20°$, and so the course that A must take has a bearing of 160°.

The minimum distance between the ships is

$\quad 100 \sin \phi = 34.2$ km.

EXERCISE 2D

1 A cruiser is moving due east at 30 km h^{-1}. Relative to the cruiser a frigate is moving on a course of 210° at 48 km h^{-1}. Find the magnitude and direction of the velocity of the frigate relative to a coastguard who is recording the paths of these ships from a lighthouse. At 1300 hours the frigate is 10 km due east of the cruiser. If both ships maintain

their speeds and courses, find the time at which the distance between them is least and their actual distance apart at this instant. Find also the time at which the frigate is due south of the cruiser. [A]

2 Two ships, A and B, are 100 km apart, with A due west of B. B is travelling west at 20 km h^{-1} and A is travelling south also at 20 km h^{-1}.

   (a) Find the closest distance between the ships in the ensuing motion if both ships maintain constant velocities.

   (b) At the time when the ships are closest a launch leaves A. Find the minimum speed of the launch if it is to intercept B.

3 At noon a boat A is 9 km due west of another boat B. To an observer on B the boat A always appears to be moving on a bearing of 150° with constant speed 2.5 m s^{-1}. Find the time at which the boats are closest together and the distance between them at this time. Find also, to the nearest minute, the length of time for which they are less than 8 km apart. [A]

4 Two ships, A and B, are 100 km apart, with A due south of B. The ship B is travelling at 20 km h^{-1} on a bearing of 120°. The maximum speed of A is 10 km h^{-1}. Find the course that A should take if it is to approach B as closely as possible, and find the shortest distance between the ships.

5 Two motorboats, A and B, are 1 km apart, with A due east of B. Motorboat B is travelling north at 10 m s^{-1}. The maximum speed of A is 6 m s^{-1}. Find the course that A should take if it is to approach B as closely as possible. Find the shortest distance between the boats and the time for A to arrive at this position.

6 Two ships, A and B, are d km apart, with A due north of B. The ship A is travelling east at u km h^{-1}. The speed of B is ku km h^{-1} (where $0 < k < 1$). Show that whatever the direction of motion of A, the minimum distance between A and B is $d\sqrt{1 - k^2}$.

7 Two ships, A and B, are d km apart, with A due north of B. A is travelling east at u km h^{-1}. The speed of B is $\dfrac{u}{2}$ km h^{-1}, and B travels on a bearing of $\theta°$ (where $0 < \theta < 90°$). If the velocity of B relative to A is in the direction Nϕ°W, show that

$$\tan \phi = \frac{2 - \sin \theta}{\cos \theta}.$$

Show that the minimum value of ϕ is 60°. Hence find the minimum possible distance between the two ships.

Key point summary

1 The position of A relative to B is given by the vector $\mathbf{r}_A - \mathbf{r}_B$, which we shall denote by $\mathbf{r}_{AB}$. The distance between A and B is given by $|\mathbf{r}_{AB}| = |\mathbf{r}_A - \mathbf{r}_B|$.   *p 14*

2 If the velocity of A is $\mathbf{v}_A$ and the velocity of B is $\mathbf{v}_B$, then the velocity of A relative to B, $\mathbf{v}_{AB}$, is given by   *p 17*

$$\mathbf{v}_{AB} = \mathbf{v}_A - \mathbf{v}_B.$$

3 $\mathbf{v}_A = \mathbf{v}_{AB} + \mathbf{v}_B$ *p 17*

4 The equation   *p 25*

$$(\mathbf{v}_A - \mathbf{v}_B)t = \mathbf{r}_{B0} - \mathbf{r}_{A0}$$

implies that if A is to intercept B then the velocity of A relative to B must be parallel to the initial displacement $\overrightarrow{A_0 B_0}$.

5 The above equation can also be used to find the time t that A will take to intercept B.   *p 25*

$$t = \frac{|\mathbf{r}_{B0} - \mathbf{r}_{A0}|}{|\mathbf{v}_{AB}|}$$

6 The following diagram shows that if $\mathbf{v}_A$ is perpendicular to $\mathbf{v}_{AB}$, then A approaches B as closely as possible.   *p 31*

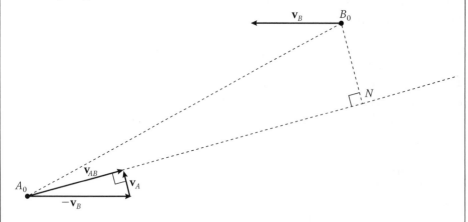

The minimum distance between the particles is given by $B_0 N$.

The time taken for A to reach the closest point is given by

$$t = \frac{A_0 N}{v_{AB}}.$$

Test yourself	What to review
1 Rachel and Katie are walking in open country. Initially Katie has position $(2000\mathbf{i} + 4000\mathbf{j})$ m relative to Rachel, where the unit vectors $\mathbf{i}$ and $\mathbf{j}$ are directed east and north respectively. Katie walks with velocity $(\mathbf{i} - 2\mathbf{j})$ m s^{-1} and Rachel walks with velocity $(3\mathbf{i} + 2\mathbf{j})$ m s^{-1}.	*Section 2.1*
(a) Find the distance between the two girls when they have been walking for 5 minutes.	
(b) Find the time when the two girls arrive at the same place and the position of this place relative to Rachel's initial position.	
(c) Find when the distance between the two girls is $200\sqrt{5}$ m.	
2 A particle A moves due east with speed 20 m s^{-1}. A particle B moves with speed 12 m s^{-1}. The speed of B relative to A is 15 m s^{-1}. Determine the directions in which B could be travelling, giving your answers as bearings.	*Section 2.2*
3 A helicopter is initially 2 km due south of an aeroplane. The helicopter travels at 70 m s^{-1} and the aeroplane travels SE at 90 m s^{-1}. Find the bearing on which the helicopter would have to travel if it were to intercept the aeroplane.	*Section 2.3*
4 A cruiser is travelling due east at a speed of 10 m s^{-1}. A patrol boat is initially 5 km NE of the cruiser. The patrol boat travels at 5 m s^{-1}. Determine the minimum distance between the patrol boat and the cruiser and the bearing on which the patrol boat should head to achieve this.	*Section 2.4*

2

Test yourself **ANSWERS**

4 1294 m, 150°.

3 065.4°.

2 041.7° or 131.7°.

1 (a) 3130 m; **(b)** $t = 1000$ s, $3000\mathbf{i} + 2000\mathbf{j}$; **(c)** $t = 900$ s.

CHAPTER 3

Moments

Learning objectives

After studying this chapter you should be able to:
- identify and calculate the magnitude of a couple
- determine whether systems of forces are equivalent
- express a system of forces as a single force acting at a point or as a single force and a couple
- determine whether a body will slide or topple, by considering the forces acting on it.

3.1 Couples

Introduction

When you studied moments in the M1 module you will have seen that if there are only two equal, parallel forces acting in opposite directions at the same point on a body, then the body is in equilibrium.

If two equal and parallel forces act in opposite directions, but do **not** act at the **same** point the body will not be in equilibrium, even though the resultant force on the body is zero. In this case the two forces form a couple.

The definition of a couple

> Two equal and parallel forces, which act in opposite directions and do not have the same line of action, form a **couple**. The moment of the couple about any point in the plane of the forces is equal to the product of one of the forces and the perpendicular distance between the lines of action of the forces. In the diagram, the moment of the couple is Pa.

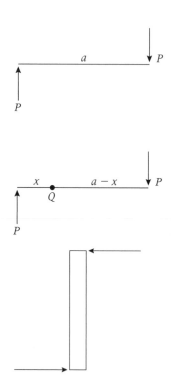

If you take moments about Q, at a distance x from one of the forces, the resultant moment of the two forces is

$$P(a - x) + Px = Pa.$$

Hence, the moment of a couple is the same regardless of the point about which you take moments.

A couple produces a turning effect. You can observe this if you place a ruler on a table and push the two ends as shown with forces of equal magnitude, you will find that the ruler will turn in an anticlockwise direction, but its centre, the centre of mass, will not move.

Worked example 3.1

Two forces, each of 10 N, act as shown on a light rod *AB* of length 8 m.

Show that the two forces form a couple and find the moment of the couple.

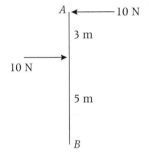

Solution

Considering the forces perpendicular to the rod, gives the resultant force as

$$F = 10 - 10 = 0.$$

So the two forces form a couple.
Taking moments about *A* gives

$$\text{Moment} = 10 \times 3 = 30 \, \text{N m}.$$

So the moment of the couple is 30 N m anticlockwise.

3

EXERCISE 3A

1 State in which of the following questions, the forces form a couple. For those that do form a couple, find the moment of the couple.

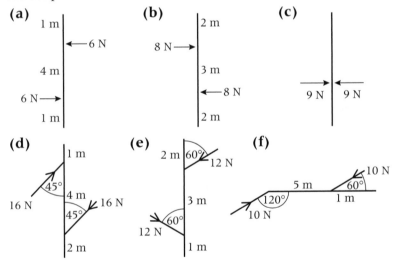

3.2 The resultant of two or more forces

Reduction of systems of coplanar forces

Coplanar forces are forces that act in the same plane. For example, a particle which is suspended in equilibrium by two strings is acted on by three coplanar forces, as shown in the diagram.

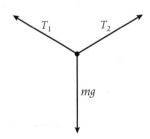

We have already seen that two coplanar forces can be equivalent to either:

(a) a single force that acts through their point of intersection (for example, in the diagram the two tensions would be equivalent to a single vertical force), or

(b) a couple, as described above.

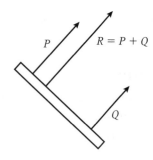

If the forces are parallel, but not equal and opposite, then the resultant is a force that is parallel to the two forces. The two parallel forces of magnitude P and Q, which act on a body as shown in the diagram, have the resultant force of magnitude, $R = P + Q$, which acts as shown in the diagram.

Forces which meet at a point

If the forces, which act on a body, and their lines of action meet at a point O, then these forces will give the same effect as a single force acting at the same point O.

If the three forces $\mathbf{F}_1$, $\mathbf{F}_2$ and $\mathbf{F}_3$ act on a body, and their lines of action meet at a point O, the three forces will give the same effect as a single force $\mathbf{F}_4$ acting at the same point O,

where $\mathbf{F}_4 = \mathbf{F}_1 + \mathbf{F}_2 + \mathbf{F}_3$.

The force $\mathbf{F}_4$ is the **resultant** of the three forces $\mathbf{F}_1$, $\mathbf{F}_2$ and $\mathbf{F}_3$.

Worked example 3.2

Three forces $3\mathbf{i} - 7\mathbf{j} + 2\mathbf{k}$, $-2\mathbf{i} + 8\mathbf{j} + 3\mathbf{k}$ and $4\mathbf{i} + 3\mathbf{j} - \mathbf{k}$ act along a body at the point P.

Find the magnitude of the resultant of the three forces.

Solution

The resultant force is:

$$\mathbf{F}_1 + \mathbf{F}_2 + \mathbf{F}_3 = (3\mathbf{i} - 7\mathbf{j} + 2\mathbf{k}) + (-2\mathbf{i} + 8\mathbf{j} + 3\mathbf{k}) + (4\mathbf{i} + 3\mathbf{j} - \mathbf{k})$$
$$= 5\mathbf{i} + 4\mathbf{j} + 4\mathbf{k}.$$

Alternatively this result can be obtained using column vectors as shown below.

The resultant force is $\begin{pmatrix} 3 \\ -7 \\ 2 \end{pmatrix} + \begin{pmatrix} -2 \\ 8 \\ 3 \end{pmatrix} + \begin{pmatrix} 4 \\ 3 \\ -1 \end{pmatrix} = \begin{pmatrix} 5 \\ 4 \\ 4 \end{pmatrix}$.

The magnitude of the resultant force is

$$\sqrt{5^2 + 4^2 + 4^2} = \sqrt{57} \text{ N}.$$

Equivalent systems of forces

> Two or more systems of **coplanar** forces, which produce exactly the same linear and turning effects on a rigid body, are called **equivalent systems of forces**.

It is often simpler to reduce a system of forces acting on a rigid body into a single force, which has the same effect.

> Systems of coplanar forces are equivalent only if:
> **(a)** the sums of the two force systems in all directions are identical in both systems,
> **(b)** the resulting moment about any point in the plane containing the forces are identical in both systems.
>
> Both of these conditions need to be satisfied if two forces systems are to be equivalent.

3

This is proved by:

(a) resolving in two non-parallel directions to make sure that the components in those directions are equal – often two perpendicular directions are used but the two directions do not have to be perpendicular,

(b) taking moments about any point in the plane.

Worked example 3.3

In the diagram below, *ABCD* is a square of side 1 m. In the first system the forces act along the sides as shown.

In the second system, the force $2\sqrt{2}$ N acts through the mid-point of *AB* and *BC*.

Show that the two force systems are equivalent.

First system

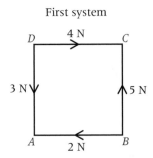

Second system

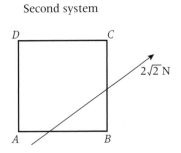

Solution

First, resolve parallel to *AB*:

For the first system, this gives $4 - 2 = 2$ N.

For the second system, the component is $2\sqrt{2} \cos 45° = 2$ N.

Second, resolve parallel to *AD*:

For the first system, this gives $5 - 3 = 2$ N.

For the second system, the component is $2\sqrt{2} \cos 45° = 2$ N.

Taking moments about A:
For the first system, the anticlockwise moment is

$5 \times 1 - 4 \times 1 = 1\,\text{N m}$.

For the second system, the anticlockwise moment about A is

$2\sqrt{2}\sin 45° \times \frac{1}{2} = 1\,\text{N m}$

Thus the two conditions are satisfied and the two systems of forces are equivalent.

> Any system of coplanar forces, which is not in equilibrium, is equivalent to either a single force or a couple.

There are four possible types of system that need to be considered. These are illustrated in the table below.

Resultant force	Moment about a point O	Comment
Zero	Zero	System in equilibrium.
Zero	Non-zero	System equivalent to a couple.
Non-zero	Zero	System equivalent to a single force acting through O.
Non-zero	Non-zero	System equivalent to a force acting through O plus a couple **or** a single force acting at a distance from O.

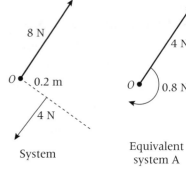

System

Equivalent system A

The first three cases have already been discussed.

An example of the fourth case is illustrated in the diagram.

The diagram shows the original system that has a resultant of magnitude 4 N and total clockwise moment 0.8 N m about O.

This is equivalent to system A, which consists of a force acting through O plus a 0.8 N m clockwise couple.

It is also equivalent to system B, which consists of a single force acting at a distance 0.2 m from O, so that it produces a clockwise moment of 0.8 N m.

Thus the line of action of the resultant force can be changed into another parallel line of action by adding a couple to the system.

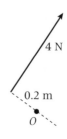

Equivalent system B

> Any system of coplanar forces which is not in equilibrium is equivalent to either:
> **(a)** a single force, or
> **(b)** a couple, or
> **(c)** a single force acting at a specific point together with a couple.

Worked example 3.4

Express the resultant of the system of forces shown, as a single force acting at a point.

ABCD is a square of side 1 m and the forces act along the sides as shown.

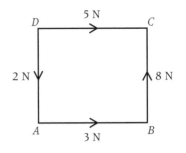

Solution

Let the resultant force have magnitude R N and act at an angle θ to *AB* through a point distance x from *A*.

Since the second system is equivalent to the first, resolving in any direction must give the same components in both systems.

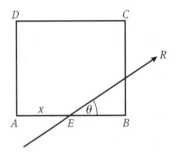

Resolving parallel to *AB*: $R \cos \theta = 3 + 5 = 8$

Resolving parallel to *AD*: $R \sin \theta = 8 - 2 = 6$

$$R = \sqrt{8^2 + 6^2}$$
$$R = 10 \text{ N}$$

$$\tan \theta = \tfrac{6}{8} = \tfrac{3}{4}$$
$$\theta = \tan^{-1}(\tfrac{3}{4}) = 36.9°.$$

Taking moments anticlockwise about *A*:

$$8 \times 1 - 5 \times 1 = R \sin \theta x$$
$$3 = 10 \times \tfrac{3}{5} x$$
$$x = \tfrac{1}{2} \text{ m}.$$

The system of forces is equivalent to a force 10 N acting through a point *E* on *AB*, where $AE = \tfrac{1}{2}$ m, and at an angle of $\tan^{-1} \tfrac{3}{4}$ to *AB*.

Worked example 3.5

The rectangle *OABC* is shown in the diagram, along with the forces that act on it. The coordinates of *A*, *B* and *C* are (3, 0), (3, 2) and (0, 2). Find the single force acting through the point *D*, which together with a couple forms an equivalent system to that shown in the diagram. The coordinates of the point *D* are (1, 0).

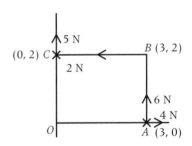

Solution

Resolving parallel to *OA*: $R \cos \theta = 4 - 2$
$$= 2$$

Resolving parallel *OC*: $R \sin \theta = 5 + 6$
$$= 11$$

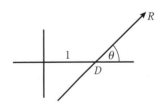

$$R = \sqrt{11^2 + 2^2}$$
$$= \sqrt{125}$$
$$= 5\sqrt{5}$$
$$= 11.2 \text{ N}$$

$$\tan \theta = \tfrac{11}{2}$$
$$\theta = \tan^{-1} \tfrac{11}{2}$$
$$= 79.7°.$$

Taking moments about O, $\quad 6 \times 3 + 2 \times 2 = R \sin \theta \times 1 + G$
$$G + R \sin \theta = 22$$
$$G = 11.$$

Therefore the system is equivalent to a force of magnitude $5\sqrt{5}$ N acting through D inclined at an angle of $\tan^{-1}\frac{11}{2}$ to the line OA together with a couple of magnitude 11 N m.

Couples

A system of three or more forces will be equivalent to a couple when the sum of the components of all the forces in all directions is zero and the forces have a non-zero moment.

Worked example 3.6

Three coplanar forces act on a light rod AB, of length $2l$, as shown in the diagram below.

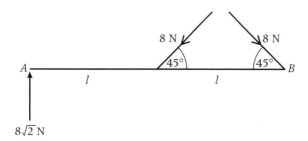

Show that the three forces are equivalent to a couple and find its magnitude.

Solution

Let the resultant force be R, acting at an angle α to AB.
Resolving parallel to AB,

$$R \cos \alpha = 8 \cos 45° - 8 \cos 45° = 0.$$

Resolving perpendicular to AB,

$$R \sin \alpha = 8\sqrt{2} - 8 \cos 45° - 8 \cos 45° = 0.$$

Hence $R = 0$ and the forces are either in equilibrium or reduce to a couple.

Taking moments about B:

$$8\sqrt{2} \times 2l - 8 \cos 45° \times l = 12\sqrt{2}l$$

As the moment is not zero, the system is not in equilibrium.

So the three forces are equivalent to a couple of moment $12\sqrt{2}l$.

Worked example 3.7

(a) Find the magnitude of the force and the equation of its line of action, which is equivalent to the three forces

$$4\mathbf{i} + 3\mathbf{j}, 6\mathbf{i} - 2\mathbf{j} \text{ and } -3\mathbf{i} + 4\mathbf{j}$$

acting at points A, B and C, which have coordinates $(5, 2)$, $(2, -3)$ and $(-1, 3)$ respectively.

(b) Find the couple, which would make the line of action of the equivalent force pass through the origin.

Solution

(a) Let the equivalent force be as shown in the diagram. Resolving parallel to the x axis:

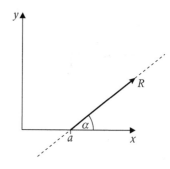

$$R \cos \alpha = 4 + 6 - 3$$
$$= 7$$

Resolving parallel to the y axis:

$$R \sin \alpha = 3 - 2 + 4$$
$$= 5$$
$$R = \sqrt{7^2 + 5^2}$$
$$= \sqrt{74}$$

Taking moments about 0:

$$R \sin \alpha \times a = 3 \times 5 - 4 \times 2 + 6 \times 3 - 2 \times 2 + 3 \times 3 - 1 \times 4$$
$$= 26$$
$$a = \frac{26}{5}$$

The gradient of the line of action is $\tan \alpha = \frac{5}{7}$.

The equation of the line of action is:

$$y - 0 = \frac{5}{7}\left(x - \frac{26}{5}\right)$$
$$35y = 25x - 182$$

The equivalent force has magnitude $\sqrt{74}$, and its line of action is $35y = 25x - 182$.

(b) Let G be the couple which makes the line of action of the force pass through the origin.

Taking moments about 0:

$$G = 3 \times 5 - 4 \times 2 + 6 \times 3 - 2 \times 2 + 3 \times 3 - 1 \times 4$$
$$= 26$$

So the moment of the couple is 26.

Note that by using a column vector approach, the resultant force **F** can be found by

$$\mathbf{F} = \begin{pmatrix} 4 \\ 3 \end{pmatrix} + \begin{pmatrix} 6 \\ -2 \end{pmatrix} + \begin{pmatrix} -3 \\ 4 \end{pmatrix}$$

$$= \begin{pmatrix} 7 \\ 5 \end{pmatrix}.$$

The magnitude of the resultant is $\sqrt{7^2 + 5^2} = \sqrt{74}$.

However in this module, you need the components of forces to be able to identify the line of action.

EXERCISE 3B

For questions **1–4**, find the magnitude of the force equivalent to the system shown.

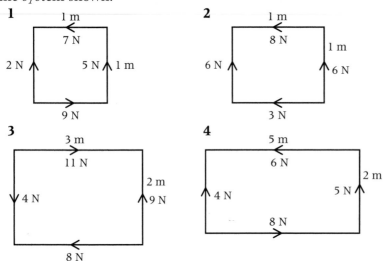

In questions **5–8**, find the magnitude of the resultant force of the forces given.

5 $\begin{pmatrix} 3 \\ 8 \\ -2 \end{pmatrix}, \begin{pmatrix} 7 \\ -4 \\ 6 \end{pmatrix}, \begin{pmatrix} -1 \\ 5 \\ 3 \end{pmatrix}.$ **6** $\begin{pmatrix} 2 \\ 7 \\ -3 \end{pmatrix}, \begin{pmatrix} -5 \\ 2 \\ -4 \end{pmatrix}, \begin{pmatrix} 6 \\ 3 \\ -2 \end{pmatrix}.$

7 $3\mathbf{i} + 5\mathbf{j} + 6\mathbf{k}$, $3\mathbf{i} - 2\mathbf{j} + 7\mathbf{k}$, and $4\mathbf{i} + 2\mathbf{j} - 6\mathbf{k}$.

8 $-6\mathbf{i} + \mathbf{j} - 8\mathbf{k}$, $2\mathbf{i} + 5\mathbf{j} + 7\mathbf{k}$, and $9\mathbf{i} - 4\mathbf{j} + 5\mathbf{k}$.

In questions **9–12**, find the magnitude of the force equivalent to the system shown and find the equation of its line of action.

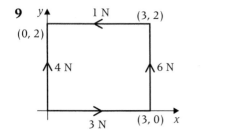 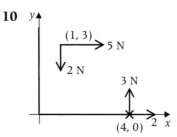

11 The three forces $3\mathbf{i} + 2\mathbf{j}$, $5\mathbf{i} + 4\mathbf{j}$, $6\mathbf{i} - 2\mathbf{j}$, acting at $A(4, 1)$, $B(3, -2)$ and $C(1, 4)$ respectively.

12 (a) The three forces $6\mathbf{i} - 2\mathbf{j}$, $3\mathbf{i} - 3\mathbf{j}$, $4\mathbf{i} + 5\mathbf{j}$, acting at $A(3, 2)$, $B(4, 7)$ and $C(1, 6)$, respectively.
   (b) The three forces $3\mathbf{i} + 5\mathbf{j}$, $\mathbf{i} - 8\mathbf{j}$, $2\mathbf{i} + \mathbf{j}$, acting at $P(7, 4)$, $Q(-8, 2)$ and $R(3, 5)$, respectively.

For questions **13** and **14**, show that a couple is equivalent to the system shown.

13   14

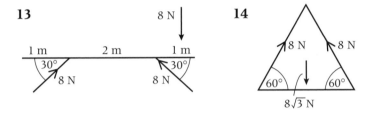

15 ABC is an isosceles triangle with $AB = AC = 10$ cm, and $BC = 12$ cm. M is the midpoint of BC. Forces act as shown in the diagram. Show that this system of forces is equivalent to a couple.

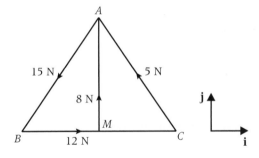

16 Forces of 2, X, Y, $(3X - Y)$ N, act along the sides AB, CB, CD, AD of a square, the length of whose side is b. Prove that they are not in equilibrium and that there is just one pair of values of X, Y for which the system is a couple. Find the magnitude of the moment of this couple.

17 Forces of 2, 4, $(X - Y)$, $(X + Y)$ N act along the sides AB, BC, CD, DA of a square of side 2 m. If they form a couple, find X, Y and the magnitude of the moment of the couple.

For questions **18–21**, find the magnitude of the force and the moment of the couple which is equivalent to the system shown. The force passes through the point given.

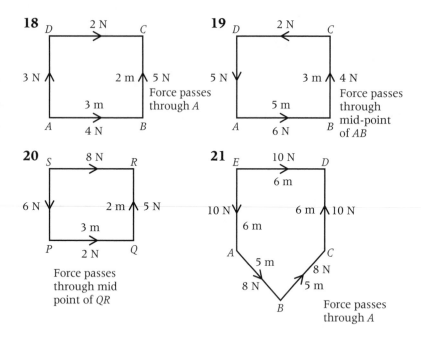

18

D — 2 N — C

3 N ↑   2 m ↑ 5 N
    Force passes
  3 m   through *A*

A   4 N   B

19

D — 2 N ← C

5 N ↓   3 m ↑ 4 N
   Force passes
  5 m   through
    mid-point
A   6 N   B   of *AB*

20

S — 8 N — R

6 N ↓   2 m ↑ 5 N
  3 m

P   2 N   Q

Force passes
through mid
point of *QR*

21

E — 10 N — D
  6 m

10 N ↓   6 m ↑ 10 N
  6 m

A   C
  5 m   8 N
8 N   5 m

B   Force passes
through *A*

3.3 Sliding and toppling

If you place a packet of cereal on a table and slowly lift one end of the table, the packet will eventually slide down the table.
If you then place the same packet on a rough mat on the table, and then lift the end of the table to the same height, the packet will **not** slide. This is because the coefficient of friction between the mat and the packet is greater than that between the table and the packet.

If, however, you continue to slowly raise the end of the table, you will find that eventually the packet will slide.

If the packet is full of cereal, you will usually find that it will topple, that is, fall over, before it slides.

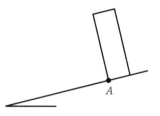

When the packet topples it will rotate about the edge *A*.

Conditions for sliding

As you will have seen in an earlier module, a body that is initially at rest, will not slide if F, the frictional force, and R, the normal reaction, satisfy $F \leqslant \mu R$.

When the body is on the point of sliding, $F = \mu R$.

Worked example 3.8

A block, of weight W, is placed on a rough surface. The coefficient of friction between the block and the surface is μ. A force of magnitude P, acting at an angle θ to the horizontal, is applied to one of the top edges of the block. The force P is increased gradually. Find:

(a) the range of values of P if the block does not move,

(b) the value of P when the block is on the point of sliding.

Solution

The diagram shows all the forces acting on the body.

You will note that the frictional force F acts in a direction to prevent movement taking place.

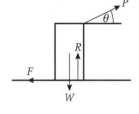

(a) Since the block will want to slide horizontally, F will act horizontally.

Before sliding takes place,

$$F \leqslant \mu R.$$

Resolving horizontally,

$$F = P \cos \theta.$$

Resolving vertically,

$$R + P \sin \theta = W$$

$$R = W - P \sin \theta.$$

Inserting the values for R and F in $F \leqslant \mu R$

$$P \cos \theta \leqslant \mu(W - P \sin \theta)$$

$$P(\cos \theta + \mu \sin \theta) \leqslant \mu W$$

$$P \leqslant \frac{\mu W}{\cos \theta + \mu \sin \theta}$$

(b) In the limiting case when sliding is about to take place,

$$F = \mu R$$

$$P = \frac{\mu W}{\cos \theta + \mu \sin \theta}$$

Conditions for toppling

First consider a body at rest on an inclined plane.

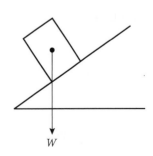

> The body will be about to topple when the centre of gravity is vertically above an edge about which the body can rotate. In this situation the weight will act through the corner about which the body will rotate, as shown in the diagram.

Secondly consider a body that is acted on by an applied force as well as its weight, as illustrated in the diagram. The body will be about to topple when the sum of the moments, about an edge at which the body can rotate, of all the forces acting on the body is zero. Note that on the point of toppling the reaction force on the body will act at the point about which it will rotate.

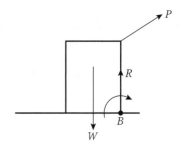

For the example in the diagram, when the moment of force P about B is equal to the moment of the gravitational force the body will be on the point of toppling about B.

Worked example 3.9

A uniform cuboid of height h and square base of side a has mass M. A force is exerted on the cuboid by a rope, as shown in the diagram. The tension in the rope is P. If the cuboid is on the point of toppling, find h.

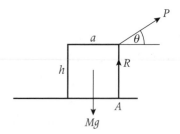

Solution

If the cuboid is on the point of toppling, the cuboid will try to rotate about the point A. In this case the reaction force will act at A. Taking moments about A,

$$hP \cos \theta = Mg\frac{a}{2}$$

$$h = \frac{Mga}{2P \cos \theta}$$

Worked example 3.10

A uniform cuboid of height h and square cross section of side a is placed on a rough plane inclined at an angle α to the horizontal. The block is about to topple. Given that $\tan \alpha = \frac{1}{4}$, find h in terms of a.

Solution

The diagram shows a vertical cross section through the cuboid, which is the rectangle $ABCD$.

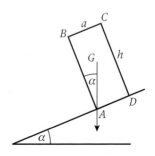

The centre of gravity of the cuboid is at G as shown. The point A is on the edge about which the cuboid will rotate.

Angle $GAB = \alpha$

$$\tan \alpha = \frac{\dfrac{a}{2}}{\dfrac{h}{2}}$$

$$h = \frac{a}{\tan \alpha} = 4a$$

Sliding or toppling

We have seen that a body will slide in certain circumstances and this depends on the value of μ. We have also seen that a body will topple and this will depend on the dimensions of the body.

> To determine whether a body will begin to topple before or after it begins to slide depends on finding the two limiting situations and deciding which situation will occur first.

3

Worked example 3.11

A block is placed on a rough plane inclined at an angle of α to the horizontal. The dimensions of the block are shown in the diagram. The coefficient of friction between the block and the plane is μ.

The angle α is gradually increased until the block either slides or topples. Show that the block topples before it slides if

$$\frac{b}{a} < \mu.$$

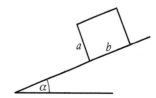

Solution

The forces acting on the block, when it is at rest, are shown in the diagram.

First find $\tan \alpha$ when the block is on the point of sliding.

Resolving perpendicular to the plane,

$$R = W \cos \alpha.$$

Resolving parallel to the plane,

$$F = W \sin \alpha.$$

On the point of sliding,

$$F = \mu R$$

$$W \sin \alpha = \mu W \cos \alpha$$

$$\mu = \tan \alpha.$$

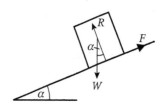

When on the point of toppling the centre of mass will be above the corner about which it will topple as shown in the diagram. In this case we have,

$$\tan \alpha = \frac{b}{a}.$$

If the block topples before it slides then the angle for toppling must be less than the angle for sliding, hence,

$$\frac{b}{a} < \mu.$$

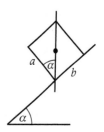

Worked example 3.12

A block, of mass m, is placed on a horizontal plane and a rope is used to pull it. The coefficient of friction between the block and the plane is μ. The rope is at an angle of 30° to the horizontal as shown in the diagram. The tension, T, in the rope is gradually increased until the block moves.

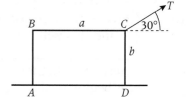

(a) Find T if the block is on the point of sliding.

(b) Find T if the block is on the point of toppling.

(c) Find a condition that μ must satisfy if the block slides before it topples.

Solution

(a) The diagram shows the forces acting on the block.

Resolving vertically,

$$R + T\sin 30° = mg$$

$$R = mg - \frac{T}{2}.$$

Resolving horizontally,

$$F = T\cos 30°$$

$$= \frac{T\sqrt{3}}{2}.$$

As the block is on the point of sliding, $F = \mu R$

$$\frac{T\sqrt{3}}{2} = \mu\left(mg - \frac{T}{2}\right)$$

$$T\left(\frac{\sqrt{3}}{2} + \frac{\mu}{2}\right) = \mu mg$$

$$T = \frac{2\mu mg}{\sqrt{3} + \mu}.$$

(b) If the block is on the point of toppling, it is about to topple about D. The moment of all the forces about A will be zero when the block is on the point of toppling and R will act at the corner D.

$$mg \times \frac{a}{2} = T \times b\sin 30°$$

$$T = \frac{mga}{b}.$$

(c) If the block slides before it topples,

$$\frac{2\mu mg}{\sqrt{3} + \mu} < \frac{mga}{b}$$

$$2\mu b < a\sqrt{3} + a\mu$$

$$\mu(2b - a) < a\sqrt{3}$$

$$\mu < \frac{a\sqrt{3}}{(2b - a)}.$$

EXERCISE 3C

1 Find the angle θ if the uniform cuboid shown is on the point of toppling. You may assume that μ is large enough so that sliding will not take place.

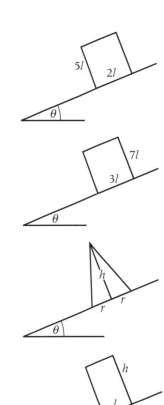

2 Find the angle θ if the uniform cuboid shown is on the point of toppling. You may assume that μ is large, so that sliding will not take place.

3 Find the angle θ if the uniform right circular cone shown in the diagram is on the point of toppling. You may assume that μ is large, so that sliding will not take place. The height of the centre of mass of the cone is $\dfrac{h}{4}$.

4 When a uniform cuboid of height h and square cross section of side l is placed on a slope inclined at an angle of $\tan^{-1}\frac{1}{10}$ to the horizontal, the cuboid is on the point of toppling. Find the relationship between l and h.

5 A uniform cuboid with square base of side $2l$, height h and density 3ρ is placed on a slope inclined at an angle of $\tan^{-1}\frac{1}{4}$ to the horizontal. The coefficient of friction between the cuboid and the slope is μ. Another uniform cuboid of height $2h$ with a square base of side $2l$ and density ρ is fixed on top of the first cuboid.

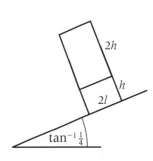

   (a) Show that the height of the centre of mass of this composite body is $\dfrac{11h}{10}$.

   (b) Find h if the solid is on the point of toppling.

   (c) Find μ if the solid is on the point of sliding.

6 A uniform cuboid with square base of side $2l$, height h and density 2ρ is placed on a slope inclined at an angle of $\tan^{-1}\frac{2}{9}$ to the horizontal. The coefficient of friction between the cuboid and the slope is μ. A uniform pyramid of height $3h$ with a square base of side $2l$ and density ρ is placed on top. The height of the centre of mass of a pyramid is $\frac{1}{4}$ of the height of the pyramid.

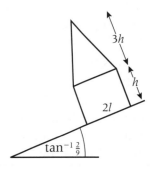

   (a) Find h in terms of l if the solid is on the point of toppling.

   (b) Find μ if the solid is on the point of sliding.

7 A uniform right circular cone of radius r and height H rests on a rough surface. The coefficient of friction between the cone and the surface is μ. The angle between the surface and the horizontal is gradually increased. Show that the cone will slide before it topples if $\mu < \dfrac{4r}{H}$.

8 A uniform right circular cylinder of height h and radius r is placed with a plane face in contact with a rough plane. The coefficient of friction between the cylinder and the plane is μ. The plane is gradually tilted.

Show that the cylinder will slide before it topples if $\mu < \dfrac{2r}{h}$.

9 A uniform solid cube is placed on a rough horizontal floor. A force which is gradually increasing is applied to the mid-point of, and perpendicular to, a top edge. This force acts as shown in the vertical cross section. The coefficient of friction between the cube and the floor is μ.

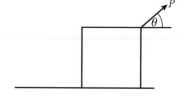

Show that the block will rotate if $\tan \theta < \dfrac{2\mu - 1}{\mu}$.

10 A block of mass 1 kg, width 40 cm and height 100 cm, rests on a table. Find the horizontal force, P, which causes it to topple when:

(a) P acts at the top of the block,

(b) P acts halfway up.

What is the least value of the coefficient of friction for which the block topples rather than slides whichever of the forces **(a)** or **(b)** is applied?

11 A right-angled triangular sheet ABC has sides $AC = 30$ cm, $BC = 40$ cm and mass 1 kg. It is placed vertically with the side AC along a horizontal plane. What horizontal force P at B causes the sheet just to topple?

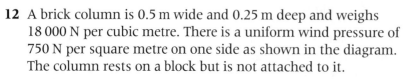

When the sheet has the side BC in contact with the plane, what horizontal force P at A then causes the sheet to topple?

12 A brick column is 0.5 m wide and 0.25 m deep and weighs 18 000 N per cubic metre. There is a uniform wind pressure of 750 N per square metre on one side as shown in the diagram. The column rests on a block but is not attached to it.

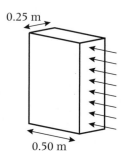

What is the greatest height the column can be if it is not to topple?

Assume the wind pressure produces a horizontal force on the column whose magnitude is the wind pressure times the area over which it acts, the force acting at the point of intersection of the diagonals of the face on which the wind blows.

3

13 A tower is made of multilink cubes, each of side 20 mm, and is placed on a plane. The plane is gently raised at one end until the tower topples. At what angle of the plane to the horizontal does a tower of 2 cubes topple? At what angles do towers of 3 and 10 cubes topple?

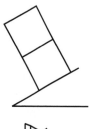

14 An equilateral triangular sheet is placed vertically with one side in contact with a horizontal plane. If the plane is raised gently, at what angle to the horizontal does the sheet topple?

15 A filing cabinet has four drawers, each of which has mass W kg when empty, the mass of the rest of the cabinet being $3W$ kg. When the bottom three drawers are empty and the papers in the top drawer weigh six times as much as the drawer itself, how far can this drawer be opened without the cabinet toppling? Treat the drawers as rectangles.

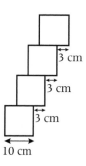

16 A pile of equal cubical blocks, each of edge 10 cm, is made by placing the blocks one on top of the other, with each displaced a distance 3 cm relative to the block below.

Show that a pile of four blocks does not topple but one of five does.

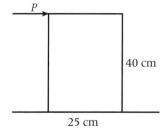

17 A cardboard box, of mass 100 g, contains 500 g of cornflakes and stands on a horizontal surface. The cross-section of the box is shown in the diagram.

P → □ 40 cm

25 cm

A horizontal force, of magnitude P, is applied to the top of the box. The coefficient of friction between the surface and the box is μ.

(a) P is gradually increased. Assuming that the cornflakes completely fill the box, show that the box slides before it topples if $\mu < \frac{5}{16}$.

(b) If the cornflakes had settled, so that there was a large empty space left at the top of the box, how would this affect your answer to (a)? [A]

18 A uniform rectangular lamina *ABCD* has width *a* m, height
   b m and mass *m*. The lamina is at rest in a vertical plane and
   on a rough, horizontal surface. The coefficient of friction
   between the ground and the lamina is μ. A force is applied at
   the corner *B* at an angle θ to the vertical, as shown in the
   diagram. The magnitude, *P* N, of the force is increased until
   the lamina moves.

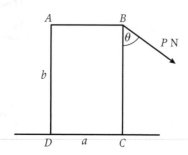

(a) Find *P*, when the lamina is on the point of sliding,
     assuming that it does not topple first in terms of μ, *m*, *g*
     and θ.

(b) Show that the lamina topples before it slides if
     $$\mu > \frac{a \tan \theta}{2b \tan \theta + a}.$$

(c) How would the inequality in (b) change if the mass of
     the lamina was increased? Justify your answer.

Key point summary

1 Two equal and parallel forces, which act in opposite directions and do not have the same line of action, form a **couple**. The moment of the couple about any point in the plane of the forces is equal to the product of one of the forces and the perpendicular distance between the lines of action of the forces. In the diagram, the moment of the couple is *Pa*.

p36

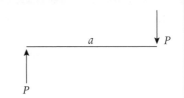

2 Two or more systems of **coplanar** forces, which produce exactly the same linear and turning effects on a rigid body, are called **equivalent systems of forces**.

p38

3 Systems of coplanar forces are equivalent only if:
 (a) the sums of the two force systems in all directions are identical in both systems,
 (b) the resulting moment about any point in the plane containing the forces are identical in both systems.

Both of these conditions need to be satisfied if two forces systems are to be equivalent.

p39

4 Any system of coplanar forces, which is not in equilibrium, is equivalent to either a single force or a couple.

p40

5 Any system of coplanar forces which is not in equilibrium is equivalent to either:
 (a) a single force, or
 (b) a couple, or
 (c) a single force acting at a specific point together with a couple.

p40

6 A body will be about to topple when the centre of gravity is vertically above an edge about which the body can rotate. In this situation the weight will act through the corner about which the body will rotate, as shown in the diagram.

p47

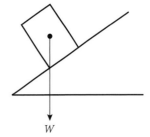

7 To determine whether a body will begin to topple before or after it begins to slide depends on finding the two limiting situations and deciding which situation will occur first.

p49

3

Test yourself	What to review
1 Two parallel forces, each of magnitude 8 N, act in opposite directions at points that are 0.6 m apart. Determine the magnitude of the couple that they form.	*Section 3.1*
2 The forces $4\mathbf{i} + 6\mathbf{j}$, $4\mathbf{i} - 2\mathbf{j}$ and $2\mathbf{i} - 5\mathbf{j}$ act at the points with coordinates (0, 2), (3, 3) and (4, 0) respectively. Show that these forces are equivalent to a single force and determine the equation of its line of action.	*Section 3.2*
3 A block has mass 4 kg and dimensions as shown in the diagram. A horizontal force, of magnitude P N acts as shown. The coefficient of friction between the block and the surface is 0.8. Determine whether the block slides or topples first as P is increased. Find the value of P when this happens.	*Section 3.3* 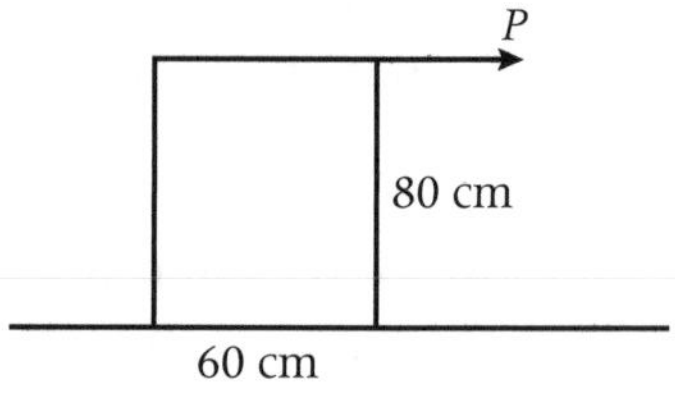
4 A cube is placed on a plane that is inclined at an angle α to the horizontal, so that the lowest edge of the cube is horizontal. The coefficient of friction between the cube and the plane is 0.9. The angle α is gradually increased. Determine whether the block slides or topples and find α when this is about to happen.	*Section 3.3*

Test yourself ANSWERS

1 4.8 Nm.

2 $10y + x = 46$.

3 Topples when $P = 14.7$ N.

4 Slides when $\alpha = 42.0°$.

Learning objectives

After studying this chapter you should be able to:
- ■ determine the external forces acting on a framework
- ■ calculate the forces in each member of a framework
- ■ decide whether the members of a framework are in tension or compression.

4

4.1 Simple frameworks

Introduction

A framework comprises a number of rigid rods, or ropes joined together.

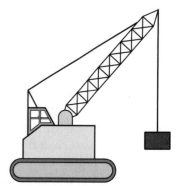

When you see a large building being constructed, you will notice that it is common to fit together a number of steel girders and thus build a large framework. After this steel framework is built, walls are then created to finish the exterior. You can see many other, different frameworks in the real world, including bridges or cranes.

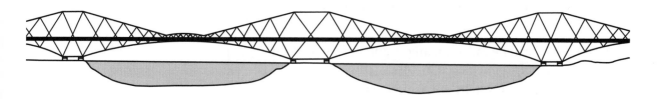

Since the beginning of time, workers have striven to make buildings safe. The Tower of Babel, a brick structure, is described in the first book of the Bible. Famous buildings from ancient history, which are still standing today, include the pyramids of Egypt, and the Parthenon in Athens. In this country, the great cathedrals built in medieval times, including Durham and York, are still standing. Visitors to Salisbury Cathedral marvel that a structure with foundations only four feet deep can support a steeple four hundred feet high. Time has proved that all these buildings satisfy the requirement that they must not break or fail.

Sometimes, however, the theory fails. The old Tay railway bridge in Scotland collapsed, and there are fears that the Millennium Bridge in London is unstable. However, we no longer make the builder pay with his life, as was the custom under the Code of Hammurabi two thousand years ago when Babylonian houses collapsed and killed the owner.

Structures can fail because the forces on the structure are too great for it to withstand. The forces may be caused because the structure itself is too heavy or because it is carrying too much weight. This is why many of our road bridges in rural areas have weight limits. Motorway bridges had to be strengthened in the 1990s when heavier lorries were permitted on British roads.

The structure can also fail if natural forces prove too strong. For example, many trees were blown over in the hurricane of 1987, and trees can be broken by the weight of snow. Similarly bridges can fail. Wind causes the Eiffel Tower to sway up to 12.7 cm.

As a bridge or a building must not fail, the structures have to be designed carefully. Engineers do not always get it right. In Durham Cathedral you can see a supporting pillar which reaches the roof in an incorrect position. The designer has to consider the cost of construction, the method of construction and the appearance of the structure. It is obvious that a bridge built from opposite sides of a river must meet in the middle. Urban office blocks would not be built in the countryside, and skyscrapers in cities must not overshadow historic buildings.

In Mechanics, a framework is modelled by a number of light, rigid, inextensible rods, which are smoothly joined together.

These rods can be called members and may, in certain circumstances, be replaced by ropes. Thus:

(a) as each rod is light, it has no mass,

(b) as each rod is rigid and inextensible, the rod is unable to bend or change length,

(c) since the rods are smoothly joined together, there is no friction at any of the joints.

Since, for example, buildings and bridges must not wobble, every framework is at rest and hence is in equilibrium. Similarly, each individual rod in the framework must be in equilibrium.

Consider one such rod *AB*. Since the rod is in equilibrium the moment about any point, say *A*, is zero. Since the rod has no mass, the only forces acting on *AB* are one force acting at *A* and another force acting at *B*.

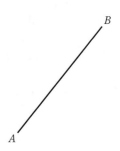

Taking moments about *A*, gives the moment of the force acting at *B* to be zero.

The only way in which the moment of the force acting at *B* can be zero is for the line of action of the force at *B* to pass through the point *A*. Hence every member of a framework only has forces acting along the member.

By Newton's law of action and reaction being equal and opposite, the forces exerted by the rod on the joint at *A* and at *B* are equal and opposite to the force on the rod *AB*.

When the forces exerted on the joint at *A* and *B* both act towards the centre of *AB*, then *AB* is said to be in compression. When the forces exerted on the joint at *A* and *B* both act away from the centre of *AB*, then *AB* is said to be in tension. When a rod is in compression or thrust, it is said to be a strut. When a rod is in tension, it is said to be a tie.

The best example to show the difference between compression and tension is to consider two different types of lights. A light may be hanging from the ceiling by a metal rod. This rod could be replaced by a flexible chain or rope and the light would still remain in position. The force in the rod from the ceiling to the light is a **tension**. If we turned the diagram upside down, so that the metal rod is resting on a base on the floor, it becomes the pole of an uplighter, as shown in the second diagram. The weight of the light tends to compress the metal rod. Obviously, the rod could not now be replaced by a chain or a rope, as the fitting would collapse. The force in the rod is a **thrust** or **compression**.

It is common that when a framework is subject to a load, some of the members of the framework will be in tension and will act as ties whereas other members will be in compression and will act as struts.

When designing a framework it is necessary to calculate all the forces acting on each member to ensure that they will support the structure.

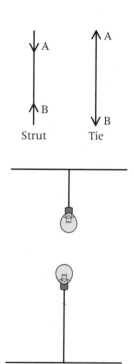

Calculating the forces in simple frameworks

A framework can be used in many circumstances including to support a weight, or to support a sign outside a shop, as in the diagrams below.

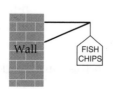

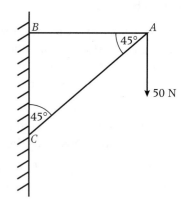

> The forces in each member can be found, because if the framework is in equilibrium, the forces acting at each joint of the framework will be in equilibrium.

Worked example 4.1

The diagram shows a simple framework. Find the forces in the two rods AB and AC, which are supporting a load of 50 N at A. State the magnitude and direction of the forces acting on the wall.

Solution

First draw a force diagram. You do not need to consider the direction of the forces in the rods. These are all initially assumed to be in tension. If a value of T is found to be negative, this would imply that the rod is in compression.

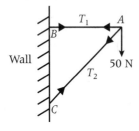

Consider the forces acting at A.

Resolve vertically

$$50 + T_2 \cos 45° = 0$$
$$T_2 = -50\sqrt{2} \text{ N}.$$

Resolve horizontally

$$T_1 + T_2 \cos 45° = 0$$
$$T_1 = 50 \text{ N}.$$

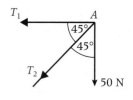

So the member AB is in tension with a tension of 50 N and the member AC is in compression with a compression of $50\sqrt{2}$ N.

The forces acting on the wall are 50 N acting horizontally at B and $50\sqrt{2}$ N acting at an angle of 45° with the upward vertical at C.

Worked example 4.2

A framework ABC is fixed to two points A and B on the ground. The framework consists of two rods AC and BC. The framework is shown in the diagram.

Find the forces acting in the rods when the framework is lifting a 30 kg mass.

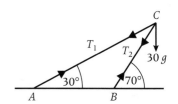

Solution

Let T_1 be the tension in the rod AC and T_2 be the tension in the rod BC.

Consider the forces acting at C.

Resolving horizontally at C

$$T_1 \cos 30° + T_2 \cos 70° = 0$$

$$T_2 = -\frac{T_1 \cos 30°}{\cos 70°}.$$

Resolving vertically at C

$$T_1 \sin 30° + T_2 \sin 70° + 30g = 0.$$

Then substituting for T_2 gives,

$$T_1 \sin 30° - T_1 \frac{\cos 30° \sin 70°}{\cos 70°} = -30g$$

$$T_1(\sin 30° \cos 70° - \cos 30° \sin 70°) = 30g \cos 70°$$

$$T_1 = \frac{30g \cos 70°}{\sin 30° \cos 70° - \cos 30° \sin 70°} = 156 \text{ N}$$

$$T_2 = -396 \text{ N}.$$

Note that since the rod AC is in tension, it can be replaced by a rope.

EXERCISE 4A

Find the forces in each of the members shown stating which are in tension and which are in compression.

1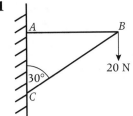

2 **3**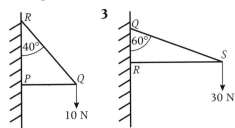

4 **5**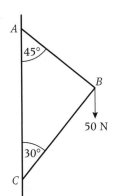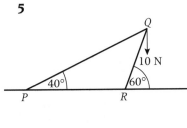

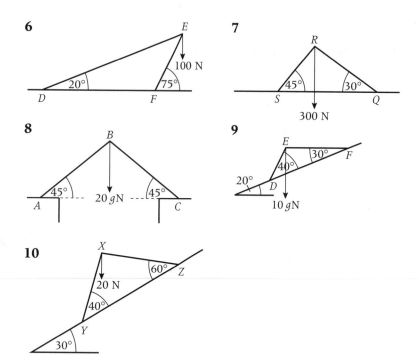

6

7

8

9

10

4.2 More complex frameworks

You can study more complex frameworks such as those found in cranes or bridges, by using the fact that the complete framework is in equilibrium, and the fact that each joint is also in equilibrium.

Worked example 4.3

The diagram shows a framework, $ABCD$, which is designed to lift a load of weight W, at D. This framework consists of four rods AB, BC, BD, and CD. In this framework the angle $ABC = 90°$, and the point B is the midpoint of AD. The angle $BAC = 30°$. The points A and C are fixed on the ground. Find:

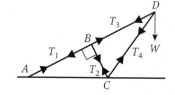

(a) the forces in each of the rods,

(b) which rods can be replaced by a rope,

(c) the forces acting on the framework by the ground at A and B.

Solution

(a) Let T_1 be the tension in the rod AB.

Similarly, let T_2, T_3 and T_4 be the tensions in BC, BD and CD respectively.

The whole framework is in equilibrium, and so the external forces acting must be in equilibrium. The external forces are the weight and the forces exerted on the framework at each of the points A and C.

Each point of the framework is also in equilibrium, so for example, the three forces acting at B are in equilibrium.

The three forces acting at point B are as shown.

Resolving along BC, $T_2 = 0$.

Resolving along AD, $T_1 = T_3$.

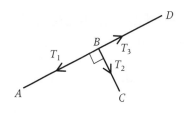

To continue we need to know the angles in the framework.

These can be calculated using the fact that B is the mid-point of AD. The angles are shown in the diagram.

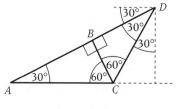

Now consider the forces acting at D.

Resolving vertically,

$$T_3 \sin 30° + T_4 \cos 30° + W = 0 \qquad (1)$$

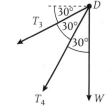

Resolving horizontally,

$$T_3 \cos 30° + T_4 \cos 60° = 0 \qquad (2)$$

Equation (2) gives:

$$\frac{T_4}{2} + T_3 \frac{\sqrt{3}}{2} = 0,$$

$$T_4 = -\sqrt{3} T_3$$

Using equation (1):

$$\frac{T_3}{2} - \sqrt{3} T_3 . \frac{\sqrt{3}}{2} + W = 0$$

$$T_3 = W$$

Hence

$$T_4 = -\sqrt{3} W$$

and

$$T_1 = W.$$

(b) The rods AB and BD are in tension and so can be replaced by ropes.

(c) The only forces acting at A are T_1, from the rod AB and the force exerted by the ground. Since the point A is in equilibrium, these two forces must be equal and opposite.

Therefore, the force exerted on the framework by the ground at A is T_1, that is W, acting at 30° to the horizontal.

Similarly, the force exerted on the framework by the ground at C is T_4, that is W, acting at 30° to the vertical.

Worked example 4.4

The framework for a bridge is designed as three equilateral triangles, *ABE*, *BCE* and *CDE* as shown. This bridge needs to support traffic crossing a river.

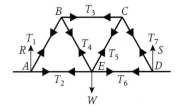

In a model the bridge can be considered as a framework which supports a weight *W* at *E* and rests on the ground at *A* and *D*. At these points vertical forces, of magnitude *R* and *S*, act on the framework. Find:

(a) *R* and *S*,

(b) the forces acting in each member of the framework,

(c) state which rods could be replaced by ropes.

Solution

(a) Let $AD = 2a$, then $AE = AB = BC = CD = DE = BE = CE = a$.

Resolving vertically for the whole system

$$S + R = W$$

By symmetry $R = S$

$$R = S = \tfrac{1}{2}W$$

[You could have taken moments about *A* for the whole system.]

(b) By symmetry $T_4 = T_5$, $T_2 = T_6$ and $T_1 = T_7$.

Resolving vertically at *E*,

$$T_4 \cos 30° + T_5 \cos 30° = W$$

Since $T_4 = T_5$, $T_4 = \dfrac{W}{\sqrt{3}} = T_5$

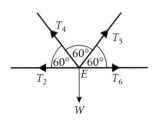

There is no point in resolving horizontally at *E* as the two unknown forces T_2 and T_6 simply cancel out.

Consider the forces acting at *B*.

Resolving vertically

$$T_1 \cos 30° + T_4 \cos 30° = 0$$

$$T_1 = -T_4 = -\frac{W}{\sqrt{3}}$$

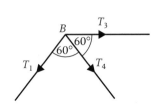

Resolving horizontally,

$$T_3 + T_4 \cos 60° = T_1 \cos 60°$$

$$T_3 = -\frac{W}{\sqrt{3}} \times \frac{\sqrt{3}}{2} - \frac{W}{\sqrt{3}} \times \frac{\sqrt{3}}{2} = -W$$

Consider the forces acting at A.

Resolving horizontally

$$T_2 + T_1 \cos 60° = 0$$

$$T_2 = \frac{W}{\sqrt{3}} \times \frac{\sqrt{3}}{2} = \frac{W}{2}$$

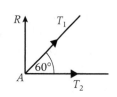

The forces in the members of the framework are:

AB $\dfrac{W}{\sqrt{3}}$ in compression,

BC W in compression,

CD $\dfrac{W}{\sqrt{3}}$ in compression,

AE $\dfrac{W}{2}$ in tension,

BE $\dfrac{W}{\sqrt{3}}$ in tension,

CE $\dfrac{W}{\sqrt{3}}$ in tension,

DE $\dfrac{W}{2}$ in tension.

(c) Rods AE, BE, CE and DE could all be replaced by ropes.

EXERCISE 4B

1 A framework consists of five light, smoothly jointed rods, PQ, PS, QR, QS and RS of lengths as shown. It is supported by a vertical force at S and a fixed support at P.

Find the forces in the members when an object of mass 20 kg is suspended from R.

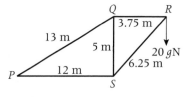

2 A framework $ABCDE$ consists of six light rods, which are in the shape of a kite. The kite is suspended from a point at A and a force of 200 N acts vertically downwards at C.

(a) Find the forces in each of the members.

(b) Which of the members could be replaced by ropes?

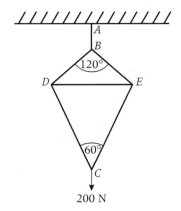

3 A framework *ABCDE* consists of six light rods, which are in the shape of a kite. The kite is suspended from a point at *A* and a vertical force of magnitude 50 N acts downwards at *C*.

(a) Find the forces in each of the members.

(b) Which of the members could be replaced by rods?

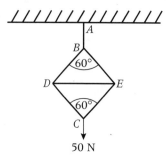

4 The framework *ABCD* consists of four light rods freely jointed at *B* and *C* and freely hinged to a vertical wall at *A* and *D*. *ABC* is horizontal and lengths *AB*, *AD* and *BC* are equal.

Find the forces in each rod, distinguishing between the struts and the ties.

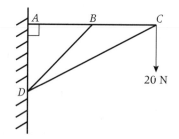

5 Calculate the force in each rod of this framework, together with the vertical contact forces indicated.

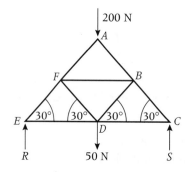

In questions **6** and **7**, the frameworks shown represent parts of a truss as used in some bridges. All rods are of equal length. Calculate the force in each rod of the framework, together with the vertical contact forces indicated.

6

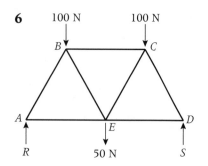

7

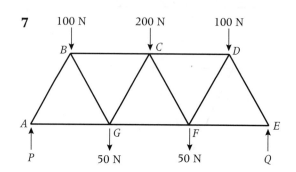

8 The roof truss in the diagram supports a roof, which can be considered to act as three separate loads of 10 kN as shown. Find:

(a) the two vertical contact forces,

(b) the forces in all the members.

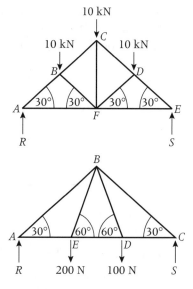

9 This framework is subject to the loads 200 N and 100 N. Two vertical contact forces support the framework. Find:

(a) the magnitude of the contact forces,

(b) the forces in each member of the framework.

(Hint: Although the framework is symmetric, it is not loaded symmetrically. **All** the joints in the framework will need to be considered.)

4

10 The diagram shows a smoothly jointed, light framework made up of equilateral triangles, that is at rest in a vertical plane, with *OD* horizontal.

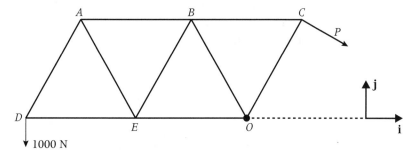

The framework is freely pivoted at *O* and the unit vectors **i** and **j** are horizontal and vertical respectively.

(a) If the force of magnitude *P* acts at right angles to *OC*, find *P*.

(b) Find the magnitudes of the forces in the members *AD*, *DE* and *AB*, stating whether they are in tension or compression.

(c) Which of the rods *AB*, *OC* and *BC* could be replaced by ropes?

(d) Find the magnitude of the reaction force acting on the framework at *O*. [A]

11 The framework *ABCD* is made up of light, smoothly jointed rods that lie in a vertical plane. The framework is freely pivoted at *D*. A force of magnitude *P* N acts vertically downwards at *A*, and a force of magnitude 1000 N acts perpendicular to *BC*, at *C*. Both forces act in the same plane as the framework, which is at rest with *AC* horizontal. The

rod *BD* has length 2 m and is perpendicular to *AC*. The angles *BAD* and *BCD* are 60° and 30° respectively. The diagram shows the framework and the forces acting on it.

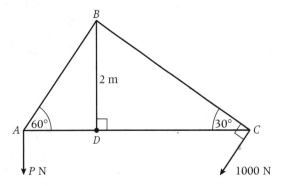

(a) Show that $P = 1500\sqrt{3}$ N.

(b) Find the magnitude of the forces in the rods *AB* and *BC* and state whether each of these rods is in tension or compression.   [A]

12 The diagram shows a framework that is smoothly hinged to a fixed point at *D*. The points *A*, *B*, *C* and *D* form a square, that lies in a vertical plane. A vertical force of 100 N is applied at *A* as shown in the diagram.

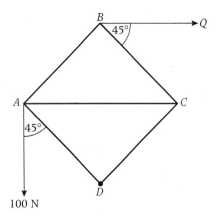

(a) What two key assumptions need to be made if you are to find the forces in each member of the framework?

(b) Find the magnitude, *Q*, of the horizontal force that acts at *B*, if the framework is to remain at rest.

(c) Show that the magnitude of the force in *BC* is $25\sqrt{2}$ N, and find the magnitudes of the forces in the other members of the framework.

(d) Which members could be replaced by ropes?

Key point summary

1 Rods can be called members and may, in certain   *p58*
   circumstances, be replaced by ropes. Thus:

   (a) as each rod is light, it has no mass,

   (b) as each rod is rigid and inextensible, the rod is
        unable to bend or change length,

   (c) since the rods are smoothly joined together, there
        is no friction at any of the joints.

2 The forces in each member can be found, because if   *p60*
   the framework is in equilibrium, the forces acting
   at each joint of the framework will be in equilibrium.

4

Test yourself   **What to review**

1 The diagram shows a framework of light, smoothly jointed   *Section 4.2*
   rods. The framework is at rest in a vertical plane with *OA*
   vertical and is freely pivoted at *O*. Two horizontal forces, of
   magnitudes 100 N and *P* N, act on the framework as shown.

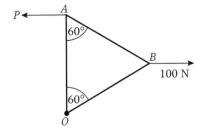

   (a) Find *P*.

   (b) Find the magnitude of the force in each member of the
        framework, and state whether they are in tension or
        compression.   [A]

Test yourself ANSWERS

1 **(a)** $P = 50$ N;

(b) *AB* : $\dfrac{100}{\sqrt3} = 57.7$ N tension

OA : $\dfrac{50}{\sqrt3} = 28.9$ N compression

OB : $\dfrac{100}{\sqrt3} = 57.7$ N tension.

CHAPTER 5

Momentum and collisions in one dimension

Learning objective

After studying this chapter you should be able to:
- use impulse and understand that it is the change in momentum
- use the relationship between force and impulse
- use the coefficient of restitution for collisions with walls
- use the coefficient of restitution and conservation to determine the outcome of a collision in one dimension.

5.1 Introduction

This chapter builds on the work that you have done in the M1 module, where you considered conservation of momentum. In this chapter we will go on to look at impulse or change in momentum and the use of the coefficient of restitution in problems involving collisions.

5.2 Change of momentum and impulse

> In the M1 module we defined momentum as the product of the mass and velocity of a body.
>
> Momentum $= mv$

Worked example 5.1

Calculate the magnitude of the momentum of a car of mass 1.3 tonnes moving at 18 m s^{-1}.

Solution

$$\begin{aligned} \text{Momentum} &= mv \\ &= 1300 \times 18 \\ &= 23\,400 \text{ N s} \end{aligned}$$

Impulse

When the motion of a body changes in some way, then clearly the momentum of the body will also change. For example, when a car is brought to rest or a ball bounces against a wall. This change in the momentum is known as the impulse.

> If the velocity of a body, of mass m, changes from u to v, then
>
> $$\text{Change in momentum or impulse} = mv - mu$$
>
> We often use
>
> $$I = mv - mu$$

Worked example 5.2

A ball, of mass 400 g, is falling vertically when it hits the ground travelling at 6 m s^{-1}. It then rebounds at 4 m s^{-1}.

Calculate the magnitude of the impulse on the ball while it is in contact with the ground.

Solution

When the ball hits the ground, we have $u = 6$ and when the ball rebounds we have $v = -4$. Then using $I = mv - mu$, gives,

$$I = 0.4 \times (-4) - 0.4 \times 6$$
$$= -4 \,\text{N s}$$

So the magnitude of the impulse is 4 N s.

Worked example 5.3

As a car, of mass 1200 kg, slows down it is acted on by a resistive force of magnitude 1800 N. The force acts for 5 s. The initial velocity of the car is 20 m s^{-1}. Calculate:

(a) the acceleration of the car,

(b) the velocity of the car at the end of the 5 s,

(c) the impulse on the car.

Solution

(a) The acceleration can be calculated by using $F = ma$.

$$a = \frac{-1800}{1200}$$
$$= -1.5 \,\text{m s}^{-2}$$

(b) Using the constant acceleration equation $v = u + at$, with $u = 20$ and $t = 5$, gives

$$v = 20 + (-1.5) \times 5$$
$$= 12.5 \,\text{m s}^{-1}.$$

(c) The impulse can be calculated using $I = mv - mu$.

$$I = 1200 \times 12.5 - 1200 \times 20$$
$$= -9000 \,\text{N s}$$

Note that the impulse is negative because the car is slowing down.

Impulse and force

For a constant force or a force that is assumed to be constant there is a simple relationship between the impulse and the resultant force on the body.

$$I = mv - mu$$
$$= m(v - u)$$

But from the constant acceleration equation $v = u + at$, we can note that $v - u = at$.

$$I = m(v - u)$$
$$= mat$$

But the resultant force, F, is related to the acceleration by Newton's second law, $F = ma$.

$$I = mat$$
$$= Ft$$

> The relationship $I = Ft$ can be used where F is constant or where F is assumed to be constant and represents the average force.

Worked example 5.4

A van has mass 2500 kg and travels along a straight road. Find the magnitude of the resultant force on the van, if it was travelling at 20 m s^{-1} and is brought to rest in:
(a) 4 s,　　　　　　**(b)** 10 s.

Solution

First calculate the impulse on the van.

$$I = 0 - 2500 \times 20$$
$$= -50\,000 \text{ N s}$$

Now use $I = Ft$ to calculate F.

(a) $\quad -50\,000 = F \times 4$
$$F = -12\,500 \text{ N}$$
The magnitude is 12 500 N.

(b) $\quad -50\,000 = F \times 10$
$$F = -5000 \text{ N}$$
The magnitude is 5000 N.

EXERCISE 5A

1 Calculate the momentum of each of the following:
　(a) a ball, of mass 120 g, travelling at 6 m s^{-1},
　(b) a car, of mass 1.4 tonnes, travelling at 50 km h^{-1}.

2 A ball travelling horizontally at 5 m s^{-1}, hits a wall, and rebounds at 3 m s^{-1}. Calculate the magnitude of the impulse on the ball if it has a mass of:

   (a) 150 g,   **(b)** 220 g.

3 A lorry has mass of 40 tonnes. The lorry is travelling at 60 km h^{-1}. As it approaches a junction its velocity is reduced to 24 km h^{-1}. Calculate the magnitude of the impulse on the lorry.

4 A ball is released from a height of 1.5 m and rebounds to a height of 0.9 m. The mass of the ball is 250 g. Assume that no air resistance acts on the ball as it moves.

   (a) Calculate the speed of the ball when it hits the ground.

   (b) Calculate the rebound speed of the ball.

   (c) Calculate the magnitude of the impulse on the ball while it is in contact with the ground.

5 The world record for the men's high jump is approximately 245 cm. Estimate the magnitude of the impulse needed for a 70 kg athlete to clear this height. Assume that the athlete is modelled as a particle that moves vertically.

6 In a test a new car is brought to rest by a concrete wall. The mass of the car is 900 kg. Find the average force on the car if it was travelling at 20 m s^{-1} and it was brought to rest in:

   (a) 2 s,   **(b)** 3 s.

7 A ball has a mass of 300 g. It is dropped from a height of 2 m. It experiences an impulse of magnitude 3 N s while it is in contact with the ground.

   Calculate the rebound speed of the ball and the height to which it rebounds.

8 A squash ball has a mass of 40 g and is travelling horizontally at 20 m s^{-1}. It hits a wall and rebounds at 12 m s^{-1}.

   (a) Calculate the impulse on the ball.

   (b) If the ball is in contact with the wall for 0.1 s, find the magnitude of the average force on the ball.

   (c) If the average force on the ball has magnitude 10 N, find the time for which the ball is in contact with the wall.

9 A ball has a mass of 400 g. The ball is moving at 8 m s^{-1}, when it is caught by a fielder. Find the average force exerted on the ball by the fielder if he takes:

   (a) 1.5 s,   **(b)** 1 s,

   to stop the ball moving.

5

10 A car manufacturer discovers that by using a new design of bumper they can increase the time taken for a car, moving at 10 m s^{-1}, to be brought to rest in a collision with a solid barrier by 10%. Calculate the corresponding percentage decrease in the average force on the car.

11 A ball has mass 100 g. It is dropped from a height of 2 m. After the first bounce it rebounds to a height of 0.8 m, then after the next bounce 0.32 m and then 0.128 m.

   (a) Find the magnitude of the impulse at each bounce.

   (b) How does the magnitude of the impulse vary in this case?

   (c) Predict the height after the next bounce.

12 A ball, of mass m, falls from a height H and rebounds to a height h.

   (a) Find the magnitude of the impulse on the ball while it is contact with the ground.

   (b) If the ball is in contact with the ground for T s, find the magnitude of the average resultant force on the ball.

   (c) Find the magnitude of the average reaction force that the ground exerts on the ball.

5.3 Impacts with walls and the coefficient of restitution

When a body collides with a wall it will rebound. The way in which it rebounds depends on the materials involved. For example a hard ball will bounce well on a hard concrete surface, but would bounce very differently on a softer grassed surface.

Experiments can be used to determine what is known as the coefficient of restitution, e.

> This coefficient of restitution is defined as,
> $$e = \frac{\text{speed of separation}}{\text{speed of approach}}$$

For a ball bouncing on the ground, the speed of approach would be the speed at which the ball hits the ground and the speed of the separation would be the speed at which the ball leaves the ground.

Worked example 5.5

A ball hits the ground travelling at 5 m s^{-1} and rebounds at 3 m s^{-1}. Find the coefficient of restitution between the ground and the ball.

Solution

$$e = \frac{\text{speed of separation}}{\text{speed of approach}} = \frac{3}{5} = 0.6$$

Note that the coefficient of restitution has no units.

Two terms that you are likely to meet are *perfectly elastic* and *inelastic*. These correspond to the cases where $e = 1$ and $e = 0$ respectively. In a perfectly elastic collision the body would impact and rebound at the same speed. In an inelastic collision the body would not rebound.

Worked example 5.6

A ball is dropped from a height of 2 m onto a horizontal surface. The coefficient of restitution between the ball and the ground is 0.6. Find the speed at which the ball rebounds.

Solution

The impact speed can be calculated using the constant acceleration equation $v^2 = u^2 + 2as$.

$$v^2 = 0^2 + 2 \times 9.8 \times 2$$

$$v = \sqrt{39.2}$$

$$= 6.26 \text{ m s}^{-1}$$

Now the coefficient of restitution can be applied.

$$e = \frac{\text{speed of separation}}{\text{speed of approach}} = \frac{V}{v}$$

$$0.6 = \frac{V}{\sqrt{39.2}}$$

$$V = 0.6 \times \sqrt{39.2}$$

$$= 3.76 \text{ m s}^{-1}$$

EXERCISE 5B

1 A ball hits the ground travelling vertically at 8 m s^{-1} and rebounds at 5 m s^{-1}.

   (a) Calculate the coefficient of restitution between the ball and the ground.

   (b) If the ball hit the ground at a speed of 5 m s^{-1}, at what speed would it rebound?

2 The coefficient of restitution between a ball and the ground is 0.7. A ball hits the ground travelling vertically at 9 m s^{-1}.

   (a) Calculate the speed at which it rebounds.

   (b) Find the height to which the ball rebounds.

3 A ball is dropped from a height of 1.2 m onto a horizontal surface. The coefficient of restitution between the surface and the ball is 0.3.

   (a) Calculate the rebound speed of the ball.

   (b) Calculate the height to which the ball rebounds.

4 The coefficient of restitution between a ball and the ground is 0.4. The ball is dropped and rebounds to a height of 1.4 m.

   (a) Find the speed at which the ball hits the ground.

   (b) Find the height from which the ball was dropped.

5 A ball is dropped from a height of 1.5 m onto a horizontal surface and rebounds to a height of 1 m. Find the coefficient of restitution between the ball and the ground.

6 A ball is dropped from a height of 2 m onto a horizontal surface. The coefficient of restitution between the ball and the ground is 0.6. Find the height to which the ball rebounds after it has bounced twice.

7 A ball is dropped from a height H onto a horizontal surface. It rebounds to a height h. The coefficient of restitution between the ball and the ground is e. Find H in terms of h and e.

8 A ball is dropped from rest onto a horizontal surface. The ball is then allowed to bounce several times. The maximum height of the ball after each bounce is 70% of the maximum height of the ball just before the bounce. Find the coefficient of restitution between the ball and the ground.

9 A ball is dropped from a height H onto a horizontal surface. It rebounds to a height h. Find the coefficient of restitution between the ball and the ground in terms of h and H.

10 A ball, of mass m, is dropped from rest at a height H above a horizontal floor. It rebounds to a height $\frac{1}{2}H$.

   (a) Find the magnitude of the impulse on the ball.

   (b) Find the coefficient of restitution between the ball and the floor.

5.4 Conservation of momentum and the coefficient of restitution

When two bodies collide momentum will be conserved. In this section we look at how we can combine this with the use of the coefficient of restitution to solve collision problems.

When two bodies collide they exert forces of equal magnitude on each other. These forces act in opposite directions, as shown in the diagram.

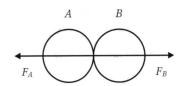

So

$$F_A = -F_B$$

If the bodies are in contact for time t, then,

$$F_A t = -F_B t$$

$$I_A = -I_B$$

Using the fact that impulse is equal to the change in momentum gives,

$$I_A = -I_B$$

$$m_A v_A - m_A u_A = -(m_B v_B - m_B u_B)$$

$$m_A v_A + m_B v_B = m_A u_A + m_B u_B$$

This result shows that momentum is conserved.

> In all direct collisions momentum will be conserved and we can apply
>
> $$m_A v_A + m_B v_B = m_A u_A + m_B u_B$$

In addition to using conservation the coefficient of restitution can also be used to form an equation to predict the outcome of a collision.

The coefficient of restitution was defined as,

$$e = \frac{\text{speed of separation}}{\text{speed of approach}}.$$

Consider the diagrams which show two bodies before and after a collision.

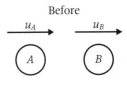

The speed of approach will be $u_A - u_B$.

The speed of separation will be $v_B - v_A$.

So

$$e = \frac{\text{speed of separation}}{\text{speed of approach}}$$

$$e = \frac{v_B - v_A}{u_A - u_B}$$

$$v_B - v_A = -e(u_B - u_A)$$

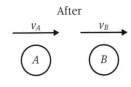

> This result,
>
> $$v_B - v_A = -e(u_B - u_A)$$
>
> can be used along with conversation of momentum to solve collision problems.

Worked example 5.7

A sphere, A, is sliding on a smooth surface towards another smooth sphere, B. Initially A is moving at $5\,\text{m s}^{-1}$ and B is stationary. The mass of A is 2 kg and the mass of B is 3 kg. The coefficient of restitution between the two spheres is 0.4. The two spheres move along the same straight line and collide directly.

Find the velocities of the spheres after the collision.

Solution

The diagrams show the velocities of the spheres before and after the collision.

First use conservation of momentum which gives,

$$2 \times 5 = 2v_A + 3v_B \tag{1}$$
$$10 = 2v_A + 3v_B.$$

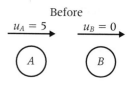

Then use the coefficient of restitution,

$$v_B - v_A = -0.4(0 - 5) \tag{2}$$
$$= 2.$$

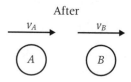

We now have a pair of simultaneous equations. These can be solved by first adding $2 \times$ equation (2) to equation (1) to give,

$$14 = 5v_B$$
$$v_B = \frac{14}{5}\,\text{m s}^{-1}.$$

This can then be substituted into equation (2) to give,

$$\frac{14}{5} - v_A = 2$$
$$v_A = \frac{4}{5}\,\text{m s}^{-1}.$$

Worked example 5.8

Two identical spheres, A and B, move towards each other along a straight line and collide directly. A is moving at $4\,\text{m s}^{-1}$ before the collision and B is moving at $3\,\text{m s}^{-1}$. The coefficient of restitution between the two spheres is 0.5.

Find the velocity of each sphere after the collision.

Solution

The diagrams show the velocities of the two spheres before and after the collision.

If the spheres both have mass m, then using conservation of energy gives,

$$4m - 3m = mv_A + mv_B \tag{1}$$
$$1 = v_A + v_B.$$

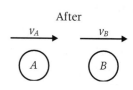

Using the coefficient of restitution gives,

$$v_B - v_A = -0.5(-3 - 4) \tag{2}$$

$$v_B - v_A = 3.5.$$

These simultaneous equations can now be solved, by adding equation (1) to equation (2).

$$2v_B = 4.5$$

$$v_B = 2.25 \text{ m s}^{-1}.$$

This can then be substituted into equation (1) to give,

$$1 = v_A + 2.25$$

$$v_A = -1.25 \text{ m s}^{-1}$$

Note that both spheres change direction during the collision.

EXERCISE 5C

1 A particle, A, of mass 250 g collides with a particle, B, of mass 150 g. Initially A has velocity 7 m s^{-1} and B is at rest. After the collision, the velocity of B is 5 m s^{-1}.

   (a) Calculate the impulse of A on B.

   (b) Calculate the velocity of A after the impact.

2 Two railway trucks, each of mass 8 tonnes, are travelling in the same direction and along the same tracks with velocities 3 m s^{-1} and 1 m s^{-1}, respectively. When the trucks collide they couple together. Calculate the velocity of the coupled trucks.

3 A smooth sphere, of mass m_A kg, moving with velocity u_A m s^{-1} collides directly with a smooth sphere of mass m_B kg moving in the same direction with velocity u_B m s^{-1}. After the collision the two spheres move with velocities v_A m s^{-1} and v_B m s^{-1}, respectively.

   (a) If $m_A = 3$, $m_B = 1$, $u_A = 6$, $u_B = 1$ and $e = 0.4$, find v_A and v_B.

   (b) If $m_A = 2$, $m_B = 3$, $u_A = 6$, $u_B = 2$ and $v_A = 3$, find v_B and e.

   (c) If $m_B = 10$, $u_A = 9$, $u_B = 2$, $v_A = 2$ and $v_B = 5$, find m_A and e.

4 A smooth sphere, of mass m_A kg, moving with velocity u_A m s^{-1} collides directly with a smooth sphere of mass m_B kg moving with velocity u_B m s^{-1}. After the collision the two spheres move with velocities v_A m s^{-1} and v_B m s^{-1} respectively.

   (a) If $m_A = 4$, $m_B = 1$, $u_A = 3$, $u_B = -1$ and $e = 0.5$, find v_A and v_B.

   (b) If $m_A = 4$, $u_A = 8$, $u_B = -3$, $v_A = 2$ and $e = 0.5$, find v_B and m_B.

   (c) If $m_B = 12$, $u_A = 10$, $u_B = -2$, $v_A = 2$ and $v_B = 4$, find m_A and e.

5

5 A sphere, *A*, of mass 3 kg moves along a smooth horizontal surface towards a second sphere, *B*, that is stationary. The mass of *B* is 1 kg. The spheres are exactly the same size and so collide directly.

    (a) If the collision between the spheres is perfectly elastic describe what happens to each sphere after the collision.

    (b) The sphere *B* then collides with the wall. After this collision, both spheres are moving with the same speed. Find the coefficient of restitution between the sphere and the wall.

    (c) What happens next?

6 A smooth sphere of mass 3 kg collides directly with a smooth sphere of mass 5 kg which is at rest. Find the condition to be satisfied by *e* in order that the spheres move in opposite directions after collision.

7 An 18 tonne railway wagon moving at a speed of 0.4 m s^{-1} to the right collides with a 34 tonne wagon at rest. Immediately after the impact the second wagon moves off with speed 0.2 m s^{-1} to the right. Find the coefficient of restitution.

8 Identical cars *A*, *B* and *C*, are initially at rest in a straight line on a horizontal surface with their brakes off. Car *A* is pushed towards the others so that it hits car *B* with speed 2 m s^{-1}. Given that the coefficient of restitution between any two cars is 0.75, find the speeds of the cars after all collisions have finished.

9 Two small uniform smooth spheres, *A* and *B*, of equal size and of mass *m* and 4*m*, respectively, are moving directly towards each other with speeds 2*u* and 6*u*, respectively. The coefficient of restitution between the spheres is $\frac{1}{2}$. Find the speed of *B* immediately after the spheres collide.   [A]

10 A small smooth sphere, *A*, of mass 3*m* collides directly with a small smooth sphere, *B*, of mass *m* which is moving in the opposite direction. The speed of *B* immediately before collision is 2*u* and immediately after collision its direction of motion is reversed and its speed reduced to *u*.

    The coefficient of restitution for collision between the spheres is $\frac{1}{4}$. Find the speed of *A* immediately before collision and the magnitude of the impulse on *B*.   [A]

11 Three identical spheres, *A*, *B* and *C*, lie on a smooth horizontal table with their centres in a straight line and with

B between A and C. Given that A is projected towards B with speed u, show that, after impact, B moves with speed $\frac{1}{2}u(1 + e)$, where e is the coefficient of restitution between each of the spheres. When C first moves, it is found to have speed $\dfrac{9u}{16}$. Find e. [A]

12 The points B and C lie on a smooth rectangular table with $BC = a$. The line BC is perpendicular to an edge of the table with C being nearer to an edge than B. Small smooth uniform spheres, P and Q, of equal radius but of mass m and $2m$, respectively, are placed at B and C, respectively, as shown in the figure.

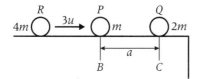

The spheres remain at rest until a third smooth uniform sphere R, of equal radius but of mass $4m$, moving with speed $3u$, collides directly with P so that the latter moves along BC with speed $4u$. Find, in terms of u, the speed of R immediately after collision and the coefficient of restitution between the spheres R and P.

Given that the coefficient of restitution between spheres P and Q is $\frac{1}{8}$, find the speed of P immediately after colliding with Q.

Given also that sphere P drops off the table before colliding for a second time with R, find the maximum distance that the point C can be from the edge of the table. [A]

13 Three small smooth spheres, A, B and C, of equal radii and masses m, $2m$ and $3m$, respectively, are placed at rest with their centres in a straight line, l, on a smooth horizontal table with B between A and C. The sphere A is now projected along l towards B with speed $5u$. Given that, after the collision between A and B, B moves towards C with speed $3u$, find:

(a) the magnitude and direction of the velocity of A after impact,

(b) the coefficient of restitution between A and B.

The sphere B now moves to collide with C and, as a result, C receives an impulse of magnitude $4mu$. Find the velocities of B and C after their collision and the coefficient of restitution between them. [A]

Key point summary

1 Momentum is defined as the product of the mass and velocity of a body.   *p70*

$$\text{Momentum} = mv$$

2 If the velocity of a body, of mass m, changes from u to v, then   *p71*

Change in momentum or impulse $= mv - mu$.

$$I = mv - mu$$

3 The relationship $I = Ft$ can be used where F is constant or where F is assumed to be constant and represents the average force.   *p72*

4 The coefficient of restitution is defined as,   *p74*

$$e = \frac{\text{speed of separation}}{\text{speed of approach}}.$$

5 In all direct collisions momentum will be conserved and we can apply   *p77*

$$m_A v_A + m_B v_B = m_A u_A + m_B u_B.$$

6 $v_B - v_A = -e(u_B - u_A)$ *p77*

can be used along with conservation of momentum to solve collisions problems.

Test yourself	**What to review**
1 A ball has mass 350 g and is travelling horizontally at 6 m s^{-1} when it hits a vertical wall. The ball remains in contact with the wall for 0.2 s and rebounds at 4 m s^{-1}. **(a)** Find the magnitude of the impulse on the ball. **(b)** Find the average force that the wall exerts on the ball.	*Section 5.1*
2 A ball is dropped from a height of 3 m and rebounds to a height of 2 m. Find the coefficient of restitution between the ball and the ground.	*Section 5.2*
3 Two spheres, *A* and *B*, have mass 4 kg and 6 kg, respectively. Initially *A* and *B* are moving in the same direction with speeds of 6 m s^{-1} and 2 m s^{-1}, respectively. The coefficient of restitution between the spheres is 0.3. They collide directly. Describe how the spheres move after the collision.	*Section 5.3*

5

Test yourself ANSWERS

3 Both continue in the same direction, *A* has speed 2.88 m s^{-1} and *B* has speed 4.08 m s^{-1}.

2 0.816.

1 **(a)** 3.5 N s; **(b)** 17.5 N.

CHAPTER 6

Momentum and collisions in two dimensions

Learning objectives

After studying this chapter you should be able to:

■ work with momentum in two dimensions
■ apply the principles of conservation of momentum in two dimensions
■ solve problems involving oblique impacts with smooth walls
■ solve problems involving oblique impacts between smooth spheres.

6.1 Momentum and impulse in two dimensions

In this chapter we will go on to extend the ideas used in one dimension into two dimensions. First we note that because momentum is a vector quantity, it has direction as well as a magnitude. In one dimension the direction is indicated by the use of a positive or negative sign. In two dimensions we will often use the **i** and **j** unit vectors, as we have done in earlier modules for kinematics and force.

Worked example 6.1

A small boat has mass 280 kg. It is travelling at a constant speed of $6 \, \text{m s}^{-1}$ on a bearing of 150°. Use the unit vectors **i** and **j**, that are directed east and north respectively, to write down the momentum of the boat.

Solution

The diagram shows the unit vectors and the direction of motion. The velocity can be expressed as,

$$\mathbf{v} = 6 \cos 60° \, \mathbf{i} - 6 \sin 60° \, \mathbf{j}$$
$$= 3\mathbf{i} - 3\sqrt{3}\mathbf{j}.$$

As the momentum is the product of the mass and the velocity it will be,

$$280(3\mathbf{i} - 3\sqrt{3}\mathbf{j}) = 840\mathbf{i} - 840\sqrt{3}\mathbf{j}.$$

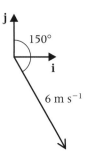

Impulse

> Impulse is still defined as the change in the momentum of a body. In two or three dimensions we would write,
>
> $$\mathbf{I} = m\mathbf{v} - m\mathbf{u} \quad \text{and} \quad \mathbf{I} = \mathbf{F}t.$$

The impulse can be represented by a vector triangle.

Suppose a ball was rolling along the ground when it was kicked. After the kick it moves at right angles to its original direction. The diagram shows the vector triangle that would represent the impulse in this case.

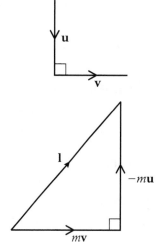

Worked example 6.2

A ball has mass 500 g. Initially it is moving at a constant speed of 7 m s^{-1}. It is then kicked, by a football boot, and moves at right angles to its original path at a speed of 6 m s^{-1}.

(a) Find the magnitude and direction of the impulse on the ball.

(b) If the ball and the boot are in contact for 0.5 s, find the average force on the ball.

Solution

(a) The diagram shows the initial and final velocities of the ball along with the perpendicular, unit vectors **i** and **j**.

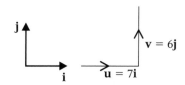

We can write

$$\mathbf{u} = 7\mathbf{i} \quad \text{and} \quad \mathbf{v} = 6\mathbf{j}.$$

Then the impulse can be found.

$$\mathbf{I} = m\mathbf{v} - m\mathbf{u}$$
$$= 0.5 \times 6\mathbf{j} - 0.5 \times 7\mathbf{i}$$
$$= -3.5\mathbf{i} + 3\mathbf{j}$$

Hence the magnitude of the impulse can be calculated,

$$\mathbf{I} = \sqrt{3.5^2 + 3^2}$$
$$= 4.61 \text{ N s.}$$

The second diagram shows the direction of the impulse on the ball. The angle α can be calculated,

$$\tan \alpha = \frac{3}{3.5}$$
$$\alpha = 40.6°.$$

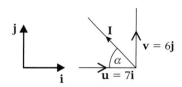

The impulse is then at an angle of 139.4° to the original direction of motion.

6

(b) The force can be found using $\mathbf{I} = \mathbf{F}t$.

$$-3.5\mathbf{i} + 3\mathbf{j} = \mathbf{F} \times 0.5$$
$$\mathbf{F} = -7\mathbf{i} + 6\mathbf{j}$$

Worked example 6.3

A ball has mass 120 g. The ball is travelling at 20 m s^{-1}, when it is hit by a racket. As a result of this it is deflected through 40° and its speed is increased to 25 m s^{-1}. Find the magnitude and direction of the impulse on the ball.

Solution

Assuming that the ball initially travels in the $\mathbf{i}$ direction gives,

$$\mathbf{u} = 20\mathbf{i}.$$

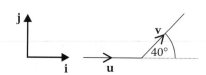

The diagram shows the initial and final velocities of the ball. The final velocity of the ball is,

$$\mathbf{v} = 25 \cos 40° \mathbf{i} + 25 \sin 40° \mathbf{j}.$$

The impulse can now be found.

$$\begin{aligned}
\mathbf{I} &= m\mathbf{v} - m\mathbf{u} \\
&= 0.12(25 \cos 40° \mathbf{i} + 25 \sin 40° \mathbf{j}) - 0.12 \times 20\mathbf{i} \\
&= (3 \cos 40° - 2.4)\mathbf{i} + 25 \sin 40° \mathbf{j} \\
&= -0.102\mathbf{i} + 16.1\mathbf{j}.
\end{aligned}$$

Now the magnitude of the impulse can be calculated.

$$\begin{aligned}
\mathbf{I} &= \sqrt{0.102^2 + 16.1^2} \\
&= 16.1 \text{ N s.}
\end{aligned}$$

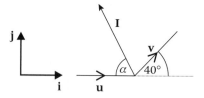

Note that the impulse is almost at right angles to the original path of the ball. The angle, α, shown in the diagram can be calculated.

$$\tan \alpha = \frac{16.1}{0.102}$$

$$\alpha = 89.6°$$

The impulse is then at an angle of 90.4° to the original direction of motion.

EXERCISE 6A

1 The unit vectors $\mathbf{i}$ and $\mathbf{j}$ are directed east and north, respectively. Find the momentum of the following:

   (a) a ship, of mass 20 000 tonnes, that travels SW at 5 m s^{-1},

   (b) a bird, of mass 300 g, that flies NE at 12 m s^{-1},

   (c) a boat, of mass 400 kg, that sails on a bearing of 200° at 3 m s^{-1}.

2 A particle of mass 0.2 kg moving with velocity $(2\mathbf{i} + 5\mathbf{j})$ m s^{-1} is struck so that its velocity becomes $(5\mathbf{i} + \mathbf{j})$ m s^{-1}. Find the impulse applied to the particle.

3 An impulse $(5\mathbf{i} + 7\mathbf{j})$ N s is applied to a particle of mass 0.5 kg moving with velocity $(3\mathbf{i} + 11\mathbf{j})$ m s^{-1}. Find the velocity of the particle immediately after the impulse is applied.

4 A particle P of mass 0.25 kg moves on a smooth horizontal table with constant velocity $(17\mathbf{i} + 6\mathbf{j})$ m s^{-1}, where $\mathbf{i}$ and $\mathbf{j}$ are perpendicular constant unit vectors in the plane of the table. An impulse is then applied to the particle so that its velocity becomes $(29\mathbf{i} + 22\mathbf{j})$ m s^{-1}. Find this impulse in the form $a\mathbf{i} + b\mathbf{j}$.

5 A particle of mass 0.2 kg is moving with velocity $(5\mathbf{i} + 7\mathbf{j})$ m s^{-1} when an impulse $\mathbf{J}$ is applied to it so that its velocity becomes $(8\mathbf{i} - 3\mathbf{j})$ m s^{-1}. Find $\mathbf{J}$.

6 A particle P of mass 0.5 kg moves on a smooth horizontal table with constant velocity $(11\mathbf{i} + 8\mathbf{j})$ m s^{-1}, where $\mathbf{i}$ and $\mathbf{j}$ are perpendicular unit vectors in the plane of the table. An impulse is then applied to the particle so that its velocity becomes $(15\mathbf{i} + 10\mathbf{j})$ m s^{-1}. Find this impulse in the form $a\mathbf{i} + b\mathbf{j}$.

7 A puck has mass 300 g. It is sliding at 6 m s^{-1} when it is hit by an ice hockey stick. After being struck the puck moves at a speed of 8 m s^{-1} and at right angles to its original direction of motion.

   (a) Find the magnitude of the impulse on the puck.

   (b) Find the angle between the impulse and the original direction of motion.

8 A cricket ball of mass 0.15 kg is moving horizontally along the line of the wickets with speed 20 m s^{-1} when it is struck by the batsman so that immediately afterwards it moves towards square leg (perpendicular to the line of the wickets) with speed 30 m s^{-1}.

   Find the magnitude and direction of the impulse applied by the batsman.

9 A puck has mass 0.5 kg. It is moving at 4 m s^{-1}, when it is struck by a stick. The stick exerts a force that is perpendicular to the original path of the puck and has magnitude 6 N. The force acts for 0.4 s.

   (a) Calculate the magnitude of the impulse on the puck.

   (b) Find the speed of the puck after it has been struck.

   (c) Find the angle through which the puck has been deflected.

6

10 A particle has mass m. It initially travels at speed u. After an impulse it moves perpendicular to its original path at a speed $2u$. Find the magnitude of the impulse on the particle in terms of u and m.

11 The diagram shows an ice hockey puck, of mass 0.20 kg, moving with speed 15 m s^{-1} and just about to be struck by a hockey stick. After being struck the puck moves in the direction shown with a velocity of 25 m s^{-1}. Find the magnitude and direction of the impulse due to the hockey stick.

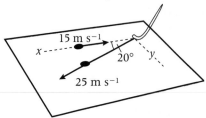

12 A ball has mass 0.5 kg and moves along the ground at 4 m s^{-1}. It is struck so that it is deflected through 60° without changing its speed.

(a) Find the magnitude of the impulse on the ball.

(b) Find the angle between the original path of the ball and the impulse.

(c) If the impulse lasts 0.8 s, find the magnitude of the average force on the ball.

13 The diagram shows a baseball, of mass 0.15 kg, travelling with a horizontal speed of 120 km h^{-1} just before being struck by the bat. Just after the impact the velocity of the ball is 200 km h^{-1} in the direction 40° above the horizontal as shown. Determine, in N s, the horizontal and vertical components of the impulse acting on the ball.

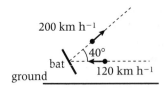

14 A tennis player strikes a ball with a racket while the ball is still rising as shown in the diagram. The speeds of the ball before and after impact are 20 m s^{-1} and 25 m s^{-1} and the directions are shown in the diagram. Given that the mass of the ball is 0.06 kg, find the horizontal and vertical components of the impulse on the ball.

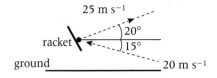

6.2 Conservation of momentum in two dimensions

Conservation of momentum also applies in two or three dimensions. In this section we will use conservation of momentum in two dimensional problems. We will not introduce the coefficient of restitution at this stage, but will use it in a later section of this chapter.

When two bodies collide they will experience impulses of equal magnitudes, but opposite directions.

$$\mathbf{I}_A = -\mathbf{I}_B$$

$$m_A\mathbf{v}_A - m_A\mathbf{u}_A = -(m_B\mathbf{v}_B - m_B\mathbf{u}_B)$$

$$m_A\mathbf{v}_A + m_B\mathbf{v}_B = m_A\mathbf{u}_A + m_B\mathbf{u}_B$$

> Momentum is conserved when a collision takes place in two dimensions.
>
> $$m_A\mathbf{v}_A + m_B\mathbf{v}_B = m_A\mathbf{u}_A + m_B\mathbf{u}_B$$

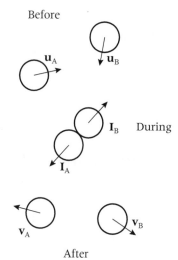

Before

During

After

6

So momentum is conserved in two or three dimensions as well as in one dimension. We do of course need to express the initial and final velocities as vectors, often using the perpendicular unit vectors **i** and **j**.

Worked example 6.4

Two cars, *A* and *B*, are approaching a road junction at 10 m s^{-1}. They do not see each other and collide. When they collide they are travelling at right angles. The mass of *A* is 1100 kg and the mass of *B* is 1400 kg. During the collision the cars become entangled and move together after the collision.

Find the speed of the cars after the collision and the direction in which they move.

Solution

The diagram shows the velocities of each of the cars before the collision and the unit vectors **i** and **j**.

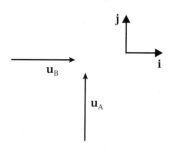

Before the collision we have $\mathbf{u}_A = 10\mathbf{j}$ and $\mathbf{u}_B = 10\mathbf{i}$. After the collision we have $\mathbf{v}_A = \mathbf{v}_B = \mathbf{v}$. Applying conservation of momentum gives,

$$1100 \times 10\mathbf{j} + 1400 \times 10\mathbf{i} = (1100 + 1400)\mathbf{v}$$

$$14\,000\mathbf{i} + 11\,000\mathbf{j} = 2500\mathbf{v}$$

$$\mathbf{v} = 5.6\mathbf{i} + 4.4\mathbf{j}.$$

The speed of the car can now be calculated.

$$v = \sqrt{5.6^2 + 4.4^2}$$
$$= 7.12 \text{ m s}^{-1}.$$

The diagram shows the velocity after the collision. The angle marked α on the diagram can be calculated.

$$\tan \alpha = \frac{4.4}{5.6}$$
$$\alpha = 38.2°$$

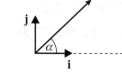

Worked example 6.5

A space capsule is travelling with a constant velocity of 120 m s^{-1}. The mass of the capsule is 2000 kg. A meteorite, which has mass 500 kg, hits the space capsule and becomes embedded in it. After the collision the two bodies move at 125 m s^{-1} at an angle of $10°$ to the original path of the capsule.

(a) Find the initial speed of the meteorite.

(b) Draw a diagram to show how the meteorite hits the capsule.

Solution

(a) The diagrams show the velocity of the capsule before the collision and the velocity of the combined bodies after the collision.

The initial velocities are $\mathbf{u}_C = 120\mathbf{i}$ and $\mathbf{u}_M$. The velocity of the bodies after the collision is

$$\mathbf{v} = 125 \cos 10° \mathbf{i} - 125 \sin 10° \mathbf{j}.$$

Then using conservation of momentum gives,

$$2000 \times 120\mathbf{i} + 500\mathbf{u}_C = 2500(125 \cos 10° \mathbf{i} - 125 \sin 10° \mathbf{j})$$

$$\mathbf{u}_C = \frac{(312\,500 \cos 10° - 240\,000)\mathbf{i} - 312\,500 \sin 10° \mathbf{j}}{500}$$

$$= 135.5\mathbf{i} - 108.5\mathbf{j}.$$

Now the initial speed of the meteorite can be calculated.

$$v = \sqrt{135.5^2 + 108.5^2}$$

$$= 174 \text{ m s}^{-1}.$$

(b) The diagram shows the initial velocity of the meteorite. The angle α can be calculated.

$$\tan \alpha = \frac{108.5}{135.5}$$

$$\alpha = 38.7°$$

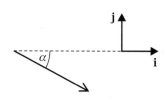

Worked example 6.6

Two particles, A and B, collide. The mass of A is 5 kg and the mass of B is m kg. The initial velocities of the particles are $\mathbf{u}_A = 3\mathbf{i} + 5\mathbf{j}$ and $\mathbf{u}_B = 2\mathbf{i} - 5\mathbf{j}$, where $\mathbf{i}$ and $\mathbf{j}$ are perpendicular unit vectors. After the collision the velocity of A is $\mathbf{v}_A = (\mathbf{i} + 2\mathbf{j})$ m s^{-1}. B travels parallel to the unit vector $\mathbf{i}$. Find m and the velocity of B after the collision.

Solution

After the collision the velocity of B will be of the form $\mathbf{v}_B = v\mathbf{i}$. Applying conservation of momentum gives,

$$5(3\mathbf{i} + 5\mathbf{j}) + m(2\mathbf{i} - 5\mathbf{j}) = 5(\mathbf{i} + 2\mathbf{j}) + mv\mathbf{i}.$$

Rearranging gives,

$$(10 + 2m - mv)\mathbf{i} + (15 - 5m)\mathbf{j} = 0\mathbf{i} + 0\mathbf{j}.$$

Considering the $\mathbf{j}$ components gives,

$$15 - 5m = 0$$

$$m = \frac{15}{5} = 3.$$

Then considering the $\mathbf{i}$ components gives,

$$10 + 2m - mv = 0$$
$$10 + 6 - 3v = 0$$
$$v = \frac{16}{3}.$$

So the final velocity of B is $\frac{16}{3}\mathbf{i}$.

EXERCISE 6B

1 Two particles, A and B, have mass m and M, respectively. Before a collision they have velocities $\mathbf{u}_A = (3\mathbf{i} - 2\mathbf{j})$ m s^{-1} and $\mathbf{u}_B = (2\mathbf{i} + \mathbf{j})$ m s^{-1}, where $\mathbf{i}$ and $\mathbf{j}$ are perpendicular unit vectors. After colliding the two particles move together with velocity $\mathbf{v} = (2.7\mathbf{i} - 1.1\mathbf{j})$ m s^{-1}.

Find M in terms of m.

2 Two particles of mass 0.2 kg and 0.3 kg moving with velocity $(2\mathbf{i} + 5\mathbf{j})$ m s^{-1} and $(3\mathbf{i} - 3\mathbf{j})$ m s^{-1}, respectively, collide and move as one particle. Find the velocity of this composite particle immediately after the collision.

3 A car, of mass 1000 kg, is travelling due north at 45 km h^{-1}, when it collides with a second car. The second car has mass 1400 kg and is travelling due east at 30 km h^{-1}. As a result of the collision the two cars become entangled and move together. Find the speed of the cars after the collision and the direction in which they travel.

4 Two snooker balls have the same mass. A white ball initially moves parallel to the side of the table at 2 m s^{-1}. It collides with a stationary red ball. The speed of the white ball is reduced to 1 m s^{-1} by the collision and it is deflected through $30°$ from its original path. Find the speed of the red ball after the collision.

5 Two particles, A and B, collide. The initial velocities of the particles are $\mathbf{u}_A = 3\mathbf{i} + U\mathbf{j}$ and $\mathbf{u}_B = W\mathbf{i} - 5\mathbf{j}$, where $\mathbf{i}$ and $\mathbf{j}$ are perpendicular unit vectors. After the collision A travels in the direction of $\mathbf{j}$ at 1.5 m s^{-1} and B travels in the direction of $\mathbf{i}$ at 10 m s^{-1}. The mass of A is 4 kg and the mass of B is 2 kg. Find U and W.

6 A football has a mass of 0.6 kg. It is moving at 12 m s^{-1} and at an angle of $30°$ above the horizontal. The ball is caught by a child of mass 40 kg. Assume that the ball and child move together after the ball has been caught. Find the speed of the child and the ball just after it has been caught and state the direction in which the ball and child move.

7 Two snooker balls collide at the centre of a table. The red ball, which was initially at rest, travels at a speed of 1.2 m s^{-1} towards a pocket at the corner of the table. The white ball was initially moving parallel to the table at 2 m s^{-1}. The size of the table is 2 m by 1 m.

Determine the final speed of the white ball and the angle between its initial and final velocities.

8 A bullet has mass 50 g. The bullet is fired at a target, which consists of a wooden block of mass 1.2 kg. The wooden block is dropped so that it falls vertically. Assume that the bullet travels horizontally. When the bullet hits the block, it becomes lodged in the block and they move together. The block was moving at 5 m s^{-1} when it was hit. Immediately after the collision it moves at 6 m s^{-1}.

(a) Find the speed of the bullet when it hits the block.

(b) Find the direction in which the bullet and block move immediately after the collision.

9 A tin can is filled with sand and placed on top of a wall. The mass of the full can is 0.8 kg. Two guns are used to fire bullets at the can, so that they hit it at the same time. The bullets have mass 40 g each and are travelling at 40 m s^{-1} when they hit the can. They become stuck in the can. One bullet travels at right angles to the wall and the path of the other is at $60°$ to the wall. Determine the speed of the can after it has been hit and the direction in which it moves.

10 A particle, *A*, of mass 2 kg travels towards a stationary particle, *B*, of mass 0.5 kg. After it has hit *B* the particles move with the velocities shown in the diagram. Determine the angle α and the initial speed of *A*.

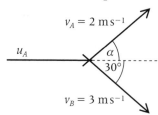

11 The diagram shows a bullet of mass 0.05 kg, moving with speed 500 m s^{-1}, just about to enter a wooden block of mass 3 kg moving with speed 10 m s^{-1} at an angle of 150° to the direction of motion of the bullet. Find, using the unit vectors shown, the velocity of the block and bullet immediately after the bullet has stopped moving relative to the block.

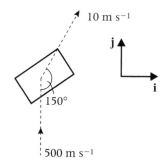

6.3 Oblique collisions with a wall

In this section we will consider collisions between bodies and smooth walls or barriers. The fact that the wall is to be assumed to be smooth is key to the approach we will take. In this case the only force that acts on the body will be a reaction force that is perpendicular to the wall. As the force acts perpendicular to the wall the component of the velocity of the body parallel to the wall will be unchanged. Also the coefficient of restitution can be used with the components of the velocity perpendicular to the wall, in the same way as it would be used for a simple bouncing ball.

> Problems involving oblique collisions with a wall can be solved using the following two principles:
> - the component of velocity parallel to the wall is unchanged,
> - apply the coefficient of restitution on the components of velocity perpendicular to the wall.

Worked example 6.7

A ball is travelling at 5 m s^{-1} when it hits a smooth wall as shown in the diagram. The coefficient of restitution between the ball and the wall is 0.4. Find the speed of the ball after the impact and the angle α.

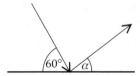

Solution

Let the speed of the ball after the impact be $V \text{ m s}^{-1}$.
As the component of the velocity parallel to the wall will be unchanged we have,

$$V \cos \alpha = 5 \cos 60° \qquad (1)$$
$$= \frac{5}{2}.$$

For the components perpendicular to the wall, we can use the coefficient of restitution to obtain,

$$V \sin \alpha = 0.4 \times 5 \sin 60° \qquad (2)$$
$$= \sqrt{3}.$$

Dividing equation (2) by equation (1) we can find α.

$$\frac{V \sin \alpha}{V \cos \alpha} = \frac{2\sqrt{3}}{5}$$

$$\tan \alpha = \frac{2\sqrt{3}}{5}$$

$$\alpha = 34.7°.$$

To find V square both sides of both equations and add them to give

$$V^2 \cos^2 \alpha + V^2 \sin^2 \alpha = \frac{25}{4} + 3$$

$$V^2 = \frac{37}{4}$$

$$V = \sqrt{\frac{37}{4}}$$

$$= 3.04 \text{ m s}^{-1}.$$

Worked example 6.8

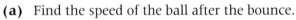

The diagram shows how a ball bounces when it hits a wall. The speed of the ball before the bounce was 8 m s^{-1}. The mass of the ball is 300 g.

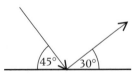

(a) Find the speed of the ball after the bounce.

(b) Find the coefficient of restitution between the ball and the wall.

(c) Find the impulse on the ball.

Solution

Let V be the speed of the ball after the collision.

(a) As the components of the velocity parallel to the wall will not be changed, we have

$$8 \cos 45° = V \cos 30°$$

$$\frac{8}{\sqrt{2}} = V \times \frac{\sqrt{3}}{2}$$

$$V = \frac{16}{\sqrt{6}} = 6.53 \text{ m s}^{-1}.$$

(b) Let e be the coefficient of restitution between the ball and the wall. Considering the components of the velocity perpendicular to the wall leads to,

$$\frac{16}{\sqrt{6}} \sin 30° = e \times 8 \sin 45°$$

$$\frac{16}{\sqrt{6}} \times \frac{1}{2} = e \times \frac{8}{\sqrt{2}}$$

$$e = \frac{1}{\sqrt{3}}.$$

(c) The impulse only acts perpendicular to the wall, so only the change of momentum perpendicular to the wall needs to be considered. Define the positive direction to be away from the wall. Then,

$$I = 0.3 \times \frac{16}{\sqrt{6}} \sin 45° - 0.3 \times (-8 \sin 60°)$$

$$= \frac{12}{5\sqrt{3}} + \frac{18}{5\sqrt{3}}$$

$$= \frac{30}{5\sqrt{3}}$$

$$= 2\sqrt{3} = 3.46 \text{ N s.}$$

Worked example 6.9

The diagram shows the directions of the velocity of a ball before and after it bounces against a wall.

Find e, the coefficient of restitution between the ball and the wall in terms of α and β.

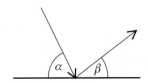

Solution

Let U be the speed of the ball before the collision and V be the speed of the ball after the collision.

Considering the motion parallel to the wall.

$$U \cos \alpha = V \cos \beta$$

$$V = \frac{U \cos \alpha}{\cos \beta}$$

Considering the motion perpendicular to the wall gives,

$$V \sin \beta = eU \sin \alpha$$

$$e = \frac{V \sin \beta}{U \sin \alpha}.$$

Using the first expression we can substitute for V in the second expression.

$$e = \frac{U \cos \alpha}{\cos \beta} \times \frac{\sin \beta}{U \sin \alpha}$$

$$= \frac{\sin \beta}{\cos \beta} \times \frac{\cos \alpha}{\sin \alpha}$$

$$= \frac{\tan \beta}{\tan \alpha}.$$

EXERCISE 6C

1 A ball has velocity $(4\mathbf{i} + 5\mathbf{j})$ m s^{-1} when it hits a smooth wall. It rebounds with velocity $(4\mathbf{i} - 3\mathbf{j})$ m s^{-1}. The unit vectors $\mathbf{i}$ and $\mathbf{j}$ are parallel and perpendicular to the wall, respectively. The mass of the ball is 0.2 kg.

   (a) Determine the coefficient of restitution between the ball and the wall.

   (b) Calculate the magnitude of the impulse on the ball.

2 The diagram shows the velocities of a ball just before and after it hits a wall.

   (a) Find the angle α.

   (b) Find the coefficient of restitution between the ball and the wall.

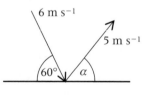

3 A ball is travelling at 4 m s^{-1}, when it hits a wall. The ball is travelling in the direction shown in the diagram. The coefficient of restitution between the ball and the wall is 0.6.

   (a) Find the velocity of the ball after the impact.

   (b) If the mass of the ball is 200 g find the magnitude of the impulse on the ball.

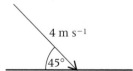

4 A ball has mass 250 g. It approaches a wall with the velocity shown in the diagram. An impulse of magnitude 3 N s acts on the ball while it is in contact with the wall. The impulse acts at right angles to the wall.

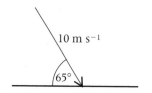

(a) Find the velocity of the ball after the impact.

(b) Find the coefficient of restitution between the ball and the wall.

5 A ball is thrown against a smooth vertical wall and immediately before impact it is moving in a vertical plane perpendicular to the wall with speed 10 m s⁻¹ at an angle of 30° to the horizontal. Given that the coefficient of restitution is 0.8, find the magnitude and direction of the ball's velocity immediately after impact.

6 A football, of mass m, is kicked to hit a smooth vertical wall.

Just before it hits the wall, the football is moving horizontally at an angle of 60° to the wall, with velocity u.

The collision changes its direction of movement through a right angle.

The diagram shows the situation viewed from above.

Modelling the football as a particle, find:

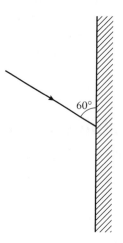

(a) the coefficient of restitution between the wall and the football,

(b) the impulse exerted on the football by the wall.   [A]

7 A ball is projected horizontally from a point above a smooth horizontal plane with speed 2 m s⁻¹. The ball first hits the floor at a point whose horizontal displacement from the point of projection is 0.4 m and the length of its first bounce is 0.6 m. Find the coefficient of restitution and the height of the first bounce.

8 A small smooth ball is dropped vertically downwards to strike a smooth fixed plane inclined at an angle α to the horizontal. The ball rebounds horizontally. Given that the coefficient of restitution is 0.6, find the angle α.

9 A small smooth sphere is dropped from a height h on to a smooth plane inclined at an angle of 15° to the horizontal. The ball strikes the plane at a point A on the plane and bounces off. Given that the coefficient of restitution is 0.8, find the horizontal displacement of the ball from A when it is next level with A.

10 $PQRS$ is a horizontal smooth rectangular billiard table with $PQ = 2a$ and $QR = a$. The smooth edges of the table are vertical and have gaps at the corners, P, Q, R and S. Balls entering the gaps are collected in pockets.

6

A ball is on the table and just outside the pocket at P. The ball is projected with speed u along the table at an angle α to PQ. After collision with the edge RS the direction of motion of the ball makes an angle β with SR. Show that

$$\tan \beta = e \tan \alpha,$$

where e is the coefficient of restitution between the ball and an edge of the table. Given that the ball now rolls straight into the pocket at Q, show that

$$\alpha = \tan^{-1}\left(\frac{1+e}{2e}\right).$$

Find a similar expression for the angle γ, between PQ and the direction of motion of the ball, at which the ball must be projected with speed u from P if it is to collide with the edge RS and then the edge PQ before rolling into the pocket at R. Show that the time taken to reach R in this case is $\dfrac{2a}{u \cos \gamma}$. [A]

6.4 Oblique impacts between two smooth spheres

When two spheres collide, conservation of momentum can be applied, but we can also apply the coefficient of restitution to the velocity along the line of centres of the spheres. For this reason it is a good idea to introduce unit vectors parallel and perpendicular to the line of centres as shown in the diagram. As the impulse between the two balls will act along the line of centre there will be no change in the components of the velocities perpendicular to the line of centres.

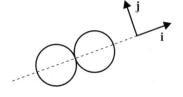

When solving problems involving oblique collisions between smooth spheres:

- note that the components of velocity perpendicular to the line of centres will be unchanged,
- apply conservation of momentum along the line of centres,
- use the coefficient of restitution with the components of velocity along the line of centres.

Worked example 6.10

Two smooth spheres, A and B, collide while moving on a smooth horizontal surface. Before the collision the velocity of A is $(8\mathbf{i} + 5\mathbf{j})$ m s^{-1} and the velocity of B is $(-2\mathbf{i} + 3\mathbf{j})$ m s^{-1}. The mass of A is 3 kg and the mass of B is 4 kg. The coefficient of restitution between the two spheres is 0.8. At the moment of impact the line of centres of the two spheres is parallel to $\mathbf{i}$.

Solution

First note that the components of the velocities perpendicular to the line of centres will be unchanged. This gives

$$\mathbf{v}_A = v\mathbf{i} + 5\mathbf{j} \qquad \text{and} \qquad \mathbf{v}_B = w\mathbf{i} + 3\mathbf{j}.$$

Now apply conservation of momentum to the components of velocity along the line of centres.

$$3 \times 8 + 4 \times (-2) = 3v + 4w$$

$$16 = 3v + 4w \qquad\qquad\qquad (1)$$

Next use the coefficient of restitution, again with the components of the velocity along the line of centres.

$$w - v = -0.8(-2 - 8)$$

$$w - v = 8 \qquad\qquad\qquad (2)$$

We now have a pair of simultaneous equations that can be solved to find v and w. Adding $3 \times$ equation (2) to equation (1) gives,

$$40 = 7w$$

$$w = \frac{40}{7}.$$

This can then be substituted into equation (2) to give,

$$8 = \frac{40}{7} - v$$

$$v = \frac{40}{7} - 8 = -\frac{16}{7}.$$

So the velocities after the collision are

$$\mathbf{v}_A = -\frac{16}{7}\mathbf{i} + 5\mathbf{j} \qquad \text{and} \qquad \mathbf{v}_B = \frac{40}{7}\mathbf{i} + 3\mathbf{j}.$$

Worked example 6.11

Two identical spheres, A and B, are free to move on a smooth surface. The sphere B is initially at rest and the sphere A moves at 4 m s^{-1}. They collide as shown in the diagram, and the angle between the velocity of A and the line of centres is $30°$. The coefficient of restitution between the two spheres is 0.4. Find the velocity of each sphere after the collision, in terms of the unit vectors $\mathbf{i}$ and $\mathbf{j}$ that are parallel and perpendicular to the line of centres.

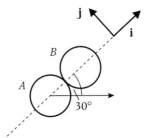

Solution

The components of the velocities perpendicular to the line of centres will be unchanged, so

$$\mathbf{v}_A = v\mathbf{i} + 4 \sin 30° \, \mathbf{j} \qquad \qquad \mathbf{v}_B = w\mathbf{i} + 0\mathbf{j}$$
$$= v\mathbf{i} + 2\mathbf{j} \qquad \text{and} \qquad = w\mathbf{i}.$$

Next apply conservation of momentum to the components of the velocity along the line of centres. Assume that the spheres both have mass m.

$$4 \cos 30° \, m = mv + mw$$
$$2\sqrt{3} = v + w \tag{1}$$

Next use the coefficient of restitution with the components of velocity along the line of centres.

$$w - v = -0.4 \, (0 - 4 \cos 30°)$$
$$w - v = \frac{4\sqrt{3}}{5} \tag{2}$$

Adding equations (1) and (2) gives

$$2w = 2\sqrt{3} + \frac{4\sqrt{3}}{5}$$
$$w = \frac{7\sqrt{3}}{5}.$$

Then substituting into equation (1) gives,

$$2\sqrt{3} = v + \frac{7\sqrt{3}}{5}$$
$$v = \frac{3\sqrt{3}}{5}.$$

Hence the velocities are

$$\mathbf{v}_A = \frac{3\sqrt{3}}{5}\mathbf{i} + 2\mathbf{j} \qquad \text{and} \qquad \mathbf{v}_B = \frac{7\sqrt{3}}{5}\mathbf{i}.$$

Worked example 6.12

Two smooth spheres, A and B, are travelling on a smooth horizontal surface when they collide as shown in the diagram. The coefficient of restitution between the two spheres is 0.5. The mass of A is 2 kg and the mass of B is 4 kg.

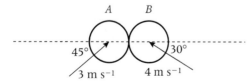

Find the speeds of the spheres after the collision and the directions in which they move.

Solution

The unit vectors **i** and **j** and the velocities of the spheres on the collision have been included on the diagram below.

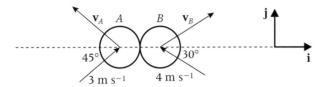

First note that the components of the velocities perpendicular to the line of centres will be unchanged.

$$\mathbf{v}_A = v\mathbf{i} + 3 \sin 45° \,\mathbf{j} \qquad \mathbf{v}_B = w\mathbf{i} + 4 \sin 30° \,\mathbf{j}$$

and

$$= v\mathbf{i} + \frac{3}{\sqrt{2}}\mathbf{j} \qquad\qquad = w\mathbf{i} + 2\mathbf{j}.$$

Now consider the conservation of momentum using the components of the velocities along the line of centres.

$$2 \times 3 \cos 45° + 4 \times (-4 \cos 30°) = 2v + 4w$$
$$3\sqrt{2} - 8\sqrt{3} = 2v + 4w \qquad\qquad (1)$$

Next use the coefficient of restitution, with the components of the velocities along the line of centres.

$$v - w = -0.5\,(3 \cos 45° - (-4 \cos 30°))$$
$$v - w = -\frac{3\sqrt{2}}{4} - \sqrt{3} \qquad\qquad (2)$$

These equations can be solved by adding $4 \times$ equation (2) to equation (1).

$$6v = -12\sqrt{3}$$
$$v = -2\sqrt{3}$$

This can then be substituted into equation (2) to find w.

$$-2\sqrt{3} - w = -\frac{3\sqrt{2}}{4} - \sqrt{3}$$
$$w = \frac{3\sqrt{2}}{4} - \sqrt{3}.$$

Hence the velocities will be,

$$\mathbf{v}_A = -2\sqrt{3}\mathbf{i} + \frac{3}{\sqrt{2}}\mathbf{j} \qquad \text{and} \qquad \mathbf{v}_B = \left(3\frac{\sqrt{2}}{4} - \sqrt{3}\right)\mathbf{i} + 2\mathbf{j}.$$

The speeds of the spheres can now be calculated from these velocities, as

$$v_A = \sqrt{12 + \frac{9}{2}}$$
$$= \sqrt{\frac{33}{2}}$$
$$= 4.06 \text{ m s}^{-1}$$

6

and

$$v_B = \sqrt{\left(\frac{3\sqrt{2}}{4} - \sqrt{3}\right)^2 + 4}$$

$$= 2.11 \text{ m s}^{-1}.$$

The spheres move in the directions shown in the diagram, where

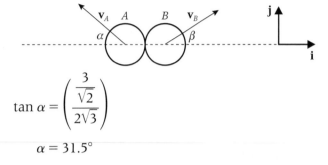

$$\tan \alpha = \left(\frac{\dfrac{3}{\sqrt{2}}}{2\sqrt{3}}\right)$$

$$\alpha = 31.5°$$

and

$$\tan \beta = \left(\frac{2}{\dfrac{3\sqrt{2}}{4} - \sqrt{3}}\right)$$

$$\beta = 108.6°.$$

EXERCISE 6D

1 A small smooth sphere of mass 0.4 kg is moving on a horizontal plane with velocity $(4\mathbf{i} + 4\mathbf{j})$ m s^{-1} when it collides with a sphere of equal radius but of mass 0.1 kg and moving with velocity $(\mathbf{i} + 3\mathbf{j})$ m s^{-1}. Given that the line of centres at collision is parallel to $\mathbf{i}$ and that the coefficient of restitution is 0.6, find the velocities immediately after collision.

2 A small smooth sphere of mass 0.2 kg is moving on a horizontal plane with velocity $(6\mathbf{i} + 5\mathbf{j})$ m s^{-1} when it collides with a sphere of equal radius but of mass 0.3 kg and moving with velocity $(2\mathbf{i} + 7\mathbf{j})$ m s^{-1}. Given that the line of centres at collision is parallel to $\mathbf{i}$ and that the coefficient of restitution is 0.25, find the velocities immediately after collision.

3 A small smooth sphere of mass 0.5 kg and moving with a speed of 7 m s^{-1}, collides obliquely with a similar stationary sphere of mass 0.1 kg which is at rest. Immediately before collision the direction of motion of the moving sphere makes an angle of 20° with the line of centres at collision. The coefficient of restitution between the two spheres is 0.5.

Find the angle through which the direction of motion of the sphere is turned by the collision.

4 A small smooth sphere of mass 0.9 kg and moving with speed of 4 m s^{-1} collides obliquely with a similar sphere of mass 0.3 kg and which is at rest. The direction of motion makes an angle of 25° with the line of centres at collision and the coefficient of restitution is 0.75.

Find the angle through which the direction of motion of the sphere is turned by the collision.

5 A small smooth sphere moving with speed v on a smooth horizontal plane collides with an identical stationary sphere. The first sphere is moving, at the instant of impact, at an angle θ to the line of centres. The coefficient of restitution between the spheres is e. Determine the velocity of each sphere after the collision, in terms of the unit vectors **i** and **j** which are parallel and perpendicular to the line of centres.

6 A sphere, A, of mass m_A, travels along the dotted line shown, with constant speed u. At O it hits a stationary sphere B, of mass m_B. After the collision the particles move with speeds v_A and v_B, respectively, in the directions that are perpendicular as shown on the diagram.

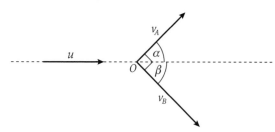

(a) Show that $\cos \alpha = \dfrac{v_A}{u}$ and find an expression for $\cos \beta$.

(b) If $\alpha = 30°$ and $m_B = 5m_A$ find v_A and v_B in terms of u.

(c) Find the coefficient of restitution between the two balls. [A]

7 The diagram shows the white cue ball, A, about to strike the stationary black ball so that it enters the pocket P. Both balls have the same mass and diameter. The coefficient of restitution is 0.7. The angle between the cue ball and the line of centres at impact is 30°. Find the angle between the line of centres and the direction of motion of the cue ball immediately after impact.

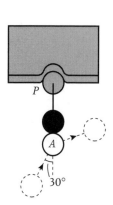

8 The diagram shows two identical smooth spheres colliding obliquely. The coefficient of restitution for collision between the spheres is 0.7. Find the speed of sphere A immediately after the collision and the angle between its direction of motion and the line of centres.

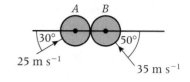

9 The diagram shows a ball of mass 2 kg falling vertically with a speed of 6 m s^{-1} when it is hit by a ball of mass 1 kg travelling along the line of centres at collision with a speed of 4 m s^{-1}. Given that the line of centres makes an angle of 50° with the vertical and that the coefficient of restitution is 0.6, find, assuming both balls are smooth, the speed of the heavier ball immediately after collision.

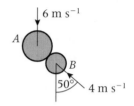

10 On a billiard table $ABCD$, $AB = 4a$ and $BC = 2a$. A smooth sphere P, of mass m, lies at rest at the centre of the table and a second smooth sphere Q, of equal radius and mass $2m$, is at rest at the midpoint of BC. Q is projected towards P with speed u and collides obliquely with P so that, after collision, P moves towards the pocket at A.

  (a) Explain why the direction of the line of centres at impact is AC.

  (b) Given that the coefficient of restitution is $\frac{1}{3}$, show that, after the impact, the speed of P is $\dfrac{16u}{9\sqrt{5}}$ and find the speed of Q. [A]

11 Two smooth spheres, A and B, of equal radius and mass, are moving on parallel paths in a horizontal plane. Sphere A has speed u and sphere B is approaching A with speed $2u$. The spheres collide and the velocity of each sphere before impact makes an acute angle θ with the line of centres, as shown in the diagram.

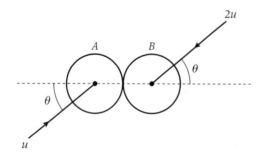

The coefficient of restitution between the spheres is e.

  (a) Find, in terms of e and θ, the velocity components of A and B along the line of centres after impact.

  (b) Use your answers to **(a)** to show that:

    (i) the direction of the velocity of *A* along the line of centres is reversed by the impact for all values of *e* and θ

and

    (ii) the direction of the velocity component of *B* along the line of centres is reversed by the collision if $e > \frac{1}{3}$.

(c) After the collision, the spheres are moving in perpendicular directions. Find $\tan \theta$ when $e = \frac{1}{4}$.   **[A]**

12 The figure shows a horizontal rectangular billiard table *ABCD* with pockets at *A*, *B*, *C* and *D*. A small uniform smooth billiard ball, *P*, is stationary at a point on the table whose distances from *AD*, *BC* and *AB* are 9*a*, 16*a* and 12*a* respectively, where *a* is a constant.

A second identical billiard ball *Q* is travelling with speed *u* on the table in a direction parallel to *DA* when it strikes ball *P* obliquely.

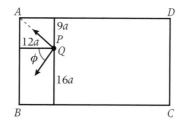

As a result of the collision ball *P* falls into the pocket at *A* and the direction of motion of ball *Q* is deflected through an angle ϕ. Given that *P* and *Q* are of equal mass and that the coefficient of restitution between the balls is *e*, show that

$$\tan \phi = \frac{6(e + 1)}{17 - 8e}.$$

Given that ball *Q* falls into the pocket at *B*, find:

(a) the coefficient of restitution between the balls,

(b) the angle between the directions of motion of *P* and *Q* immediately after the impact.   **[A]**

13 The figure shows the positions of two uniform smooth spheres, *A* and *B*, at the instant they collide. The spheres are of the same radius but of mass *m* and 2*m* respectively. Immediately before collision, *A* and *B* have speeds 15*u* and 5*u* in perpendicular directions, as shown in the figure. The line of centres makes an angle θ with the direction of motion of *A*, where $\sin \theta = \frac{4}{5}$. Given that the coefficient of restitution between the spheres is $\frac{1}{5}$:

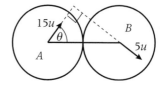

(a) show that the speed of *B* immediately after collision is $3u\sqrt{5}$, and find

(b) the impulse on *B*.   **[A]**

Key point summary

1 Impulse is still defined as the change in the momentum of a body. In two or three dimensions we would write,   *p85*

$$\mathbf{I} = m\mathbf{v} - m\mathbf{u} \qquad \text{and} \qquad \mathbf{i} = \mathbf{F}t.$$

2 Momentum is conserved when a collision takes place in two dimensions.   *p89*

$$m_A\mathbf{v}_A + m_B\mathbf{u}_B = m_A\mathbf{u}_A + m_B\mathbf{u}_B$$

3 Problems involving oblique collisions with a wall can be solved using the following two principles: *p93*

- the component of velocity parallel to the wall is unchanged,
- apply the coefficient of restitution to the components of velocity perpendicular to the wall.

4 When solving problems involving oblique collisions between smooth spheres: *p98*

- note that the components of velocity perpendicular to the line of centres will be unchanged,
- apply conservation of momentum along the line of centres,
- use the coefficient of restitution with the components of velocity along the line of centres.

Test yourself | What to review

1 A bat exerts a force on a ball of mass 0.3 kg. The speed of the ball increases from 4 m s^{-1} to 9 m s^{-1} and the direction of the motion of the ball changes as shown in the diagram.

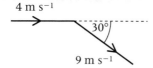

4 m s^{-1}

30°

9 m s^{-1}

Section 6.1

(a) Calculate the magnitude of the impulse on the ball.

(b) Given that the ball is in contact with the bat for 0.1 s, find the magnitude of the average force on the ball.

2 Two particles, *A* and *B*, have mass 2 kg and 5 kg, respectively. Before they collide *A* has velocity $(4\mathbf{i} + 7\mathbf{j})$ m s^{-1}. The two spheres collide and then *A* moves with velocity $(2\mathbf{i} - 4\mathbf{j})$ m s^{-1} and *B* moves with velocity $(\mathbf{i} + \mathbf{j})$ m s^{-1}. The unit vectors $\mathbf{i}$ and $\mathbf{j}$ are perpendicular.

Find the speed of *B* before the collision.

Section 6.2

3 A ball is travelling at 5 m s^{-1} when it hits a smooth wall, as shown in the diagram. The coefficient of restitution between the ball and the wall is 0.6.

(a) Determine the speed of the ball after the impact.

(b) Calculate the angle between the wall and the velocity of the ball after the impact.

Section 6.3

50°

4 Two smooth spheres collide as shown in the diagram. The mass of *A* is 0.5 kg and the mass of *B* is 0.3 kg. The coefficient of restitution between the spheres is 0.4. Find the speed of each sphere after the collision.

Section 6.4

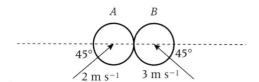

A *B*

45° 45°

2 m s^{-1} 3 m s^{-1}

6

4 1.48 m s^{-1}, 2.33 m s^{-1}.

3 (a) 3.95 m s^{-1}; **(b)** 35.6°.

2 3.41 m s^{-1}.

1 (a) 1.77 N s; **(b)** 17.7 N.

Exam style practice paper

Time allowed 1 hour 15 minutes

Answer **all** questions

1 As a sphere, of mass m, falls it experiences a resistance force. The magnitude of this force depends on the speed v of the sphere. Two models are proposed for the magnitude of the resistance force.

(a) Given that the resistance force has magnitude mkv where k is a constant, determine the dimensions of k in terms of M, L and T. *(3 marks)*

(b) In an alternative model the resistance has magnitude mKv^n, where K and n are constants. Determine n if K has dimensions $L^{-\frac{1}{2}}T^{-\frac{1}{2}}$. *(3 marks)*

2 The diagram shows a framework, which is made up of light, pin jointed members. Each of the triangles in the framework is an equilateral triangle. The framework is in equilibrium in a vertical plane.

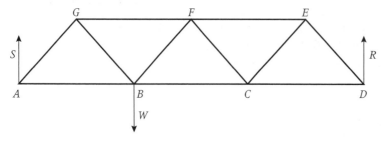

A load of weight W N is suspended from the framework at B. Reaction forces of magnitude R and S act on the framework at A and D.

(a) Find R and S. *(3 marks)*

(b) Determine the magnitudes of the forces in the members AG, AB and BG, in terms of W. State which of these members are in compression and which are in tension. *(6 marks)*

3 Three identical spheres, A, B and C, are initially at rest, in that order, along a straight horizontal line. The sphere A is set into motion so that it moves along the line at 2 m s^{-1} towards B. The coefficient of restitution between the spheres is 0.4.

(a) Show that after the collision between A and B the sphere A moves in the same direction with a speed of $0.6\,\text{m s}^{-1}$. *(4 marks)*

(b) Find the speed of B after the collision. *(2 marks)*

The sphere B then collides with the sphere C.

(c) Determine how these spheres move after this collision. *(5 marks)*

(d) Describe the next collision that will take place. *(1 mark)*

4 A ship sails north east at a constant speed of $12\,\text{km h}^{-1}$. At 1200 a patrol boat is 40 km due west of the ship. The patrol boat travels at a speed of $15\,\text{km h}^{-1}$. The patrol boat travels so as to intercept the ship in the minimum time.

(a) Determine the bearing on which the patrol boat should travel to intercept the ship in the shortest time. *(5 marks)*

(b) Calculate the time, to the nearest minute, when the patrol boat intercepts the ship and the distance of the ship from its initial position at this time. *(5 marks)*

5 The diagram shows a uniform lamina that is initially at rest in a vertical plane, the edge AB on a horizontal surface.

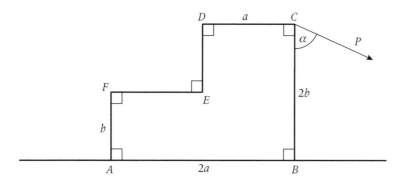

The lamina is such that the length of AB is $2a$, the length of BC is $2b$, the length of CD is a and the length of AF is b. The mass of the lamina is m. The coefficient of friction between the lamina and the surface is μ.

A force of magnitude P acts on the lamina as shown in the diagram. This force is gradually increased until the lamina moves.

(a) Show that the centre of mass is at a distance $\dfrac{5a}{6}$ from BC. *(3 marks)*

(b) Show that the lamina is on the point of toppling when

$$P = \frac{5mga}{12b\sin\alpha}.$$

(2 marks)

(c) Show that the lamina is on the point of sliding when

$$P = \frac{\mu mg}{\sin \alpha - \mu \cos \alpha}.$$ *(4 marks)*

(d) Find an inequality that μ must satisfy if the lamina is to slide before it topples. *(4 marks)*

6 A sphere, A, of mass 2 kg is travelling at 5 m s^{-1}, when it hits a stationary sphere, B, of mass 1 kg. The diagram shows the line of centres of the spheres and the initial velocity of the moving sphere. The coefficient of restitution between the two spheres is 0.6.

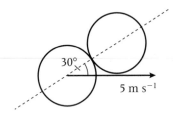

Find the speed of each sphere after the collision. *(10 marks)*

Answers

1 Dimensional analysis

EXERCISE 1A

1   **(a)** ML^2T^{-2}; **(b)** ML^2T^{-2}; **(c)** MLT^{-1}; **(d)** $ML^{-1}T^{-2}$;
    (e) ML^{-3}; **(f)** ML^{-2}.

2   $[\lambda] = MLT^{-2}$, $[E] = ML^2T^{-2}$.

3   **(a)** Yes; **(b)** Yes; **(c)** No; **(d)** Yes.

4   L^{-1}.

6   **(a)** $[k] = T^{-1}$, $[A] = L$, B is dimensionless.

    (b) $[A] = LT^{-1}$, $[B] = LT^{-2}$;

    (c) $[k] = T^{-1}$, $[A] = LT^{-2}$, $[B] = LT^{-2}$;

    (d) $[A] = T^{-2}$, $[B] = T^{-1}$.

EXERCISE 1B

1   $x = -1, y = \frac{1}{2}, z = -\frac{1}{2}$.

2   **(a)** $T = k\sqrt{\dfrac{\sqrt{A}}{g}}$; **(b)** 3.13; **(c)** increase by a factor of $\sqrt{2}$.

3   $x = 2, y = 3, z = 1$.

4   **(a)** $f = \dfrac{k}{l}\sqrt{\dfrac{T}{\rho}}$; **(b)** increase by a factor of $\sqrt{2}$.

5   $p = 0, q = -4, r = 1$.

6   $P = k\rho gh$.

7   $P = k\sqrt{\dfrac{R^3}{GM}}$.

8   **(a)** $x = \frac{1}{2}, y = -\frac{1}{2}$; **(b)** 6.43, 1.95 s.

9   $a = \frac{1}{2}, b = \frac{1}{2}, c = -\frac{1}{2}$.

10 **(a)** ML^{-3}; **(b)** $a = \frac{1}{2}, b = \frac{1}{2}, c = 0$; **(c)** Speed is halved.

2 Relative motion

EXERCISE 2A

1   3 s.

2   **(a)** $11\mathbf{i} + 3\mathbf{j}$ m;   **(b)** 32.5°.

3   **(a)** $\mathbf{r}_A = (9t - 9)\mathbf{i} + (7t - 5)\mathbf{j}$.
     (b) $\mathbf{r}_B = 5.4t\mathbf{i} + 5t\mathbf{j}$.
     (c) $t = 2.5$ hours.

4   **(a)** $\mathbf{r}_{AB} = (3t - 8000)\mathbf{i} - 4t\mathbf{j}$;
     (b) 6.4 km;
     (c) 393 s to 1527 s.

5    $610 - 25t$, $610 - 20t$, 26.8 s.

6    $(52 - 7t)\mathbf{i} - \sqrt{3}t\mathbf{j}$, $2\sqrt{39}$ m, 7 s.

7    $\mathbf{r}_A = -20t\mathbf{i}$, $\mathbf{r}_B = \frac{1}{5}[-64t\mathbf{i} + (48t - 6)\mathbf{j}]$, 4.8 minutes past noon.

EXERCISE 2B

1   **(a)** $(-250\mathbf{i} - 550\mathbf{j} + 10\mathbf{k})$ km h^{-1};
     (b) $(250\mathbf{i} + 550\mathbf{j} - 10\mathbf{k})$ km h^{-1}.

2   338°.

3    $(18\mathbf{i} + 10\mathbf{j})$ km h^{-1}.

4    $\mathbf{v}_A = (6\mathbf{i} + 6\mathbf{j})$ km h^{-1}, $\mathbf{v}_B = (2\mathbf{i} + 3\mathbf{j})$ km h^{-1}.

5    $\mathbf{v}_A = (13.6\mathbf{i} + 20.4\mathbf{j})$ km h^{-1}, $\mathbf{v}_B = (3.6\mathbf{i} - 3.6\mathbf{j})$ km h^{-1}.

6   10.3 km h^{-1}, 043.1°.

7   13.1 m s^{-1}.

8   49.5°

9   26.5 m s^{-1}.

10   1.93:1.

11   35:13.

12   084.3°, 497 km h^{-1}, 4.02 h.

13   60° to bank upstream, 28.9 s.

14   25 s, 50 m.

15   125 s, 100 s, 300 m.

16   53.1° or 20.6° upstream.

17 (a) Due north, 100 s, $100\sqrt{34}$ m;
   (b) 53.1° to the bank upstream, 125 s, 500 m.

18 293.7 km h^{-1}.

19 $\sqrt{58}$ m, $(6\mathbf{i} + 8\mathbf{j})$ km h^{-1}.

20 $(4\mathbf{i} + 7\mathbf{j})$ m s^{-1}.

21 $(2\mathbf{i} + 2\mathbf{j})$ km h^{-1}, $-2\mathbf{j}$ km h^{-1}, $\mathbf{v}_A = (4\mathbf{i} + 2\mathbf{j})$ km h^{-1} or $2\sqrt{5}$ km h^{-1} on 063.4°.

22 33 mph on 042°, $(22.5\mathbf{i} + 24.6\mathbf{j})$ mph.

23 (a) $(-450\mathbf{i} + 150\mathbf{j} + 0.1\mathbf{k})$ mph;
   (b) $(5\mathbf{i} + 25\mathbf{j} + 0.41\mathbf{k})$ miles;
   (c) $\sqrt{(50 - 450t)^2 + (10 + 150t)^2 + (0.4 + 0.1t)^2}$ miles;
   (d) 12:21, 25.3 miles.

EXERCISE 2C

1 339.4°, 1 hour 21 minutes.

2 150 km or 66.8 km

3 060°.

4 (a) 260°, 5 hours;   **(b)** 206° or 254°.

5 (a) $-20\mathbf{i} + 5t\mathbf{j}$, $ut\mathbf{i} + vt\mathbf{j}$;   **(b)** 12 minutes, 273°.

6 $12\mathbf{i} - 5\mathbf{j}$, $(30, -10)$, 80 s.

7 $\mathbf{i} - \mathbf{j}$, $(15, 10)$, 5, $\frac{1}{17}(23\mathbf{i} + 7\mathbf{j})$, $(20\frac{5}{11}, 18\frac{2}{11})$, $7\frac{8}{11}$.

8 $6\mathbf{i} + 8\mathbf{j}$, 25 s, $150\mathbf{i} + 200\mathbf{j}$.

9 $h = 50$.

10 (a) $(2.5\mathbf{i} - 2\mathbf{j})$ m s^{-1};   **(b)** 7.2 km;   **(c)** 1300 hours.

EXERCISE 2D

1 42 km h^{-1} on 172°, 1306 hours, 8.66 km, 1325 hours.

2 (a) $50\sqrt{2}$ km;   **(b)** $10\sqrt{2}$ km h^{-1}.

3 12:30, $4.5\sqrt{3}$ km, 24 minutes.

4 060°, 50 km.

5 307°, 800 m, 75 s.

7 $d\dfrac{\sqrt{3}}{2}$.

3 Moments

EXERCISE 3A

1 **(a)** Yes, 24 N m; **(b)** Yes, 24 N m; **(c)** No; **(d)** Yes, $32\sqrt{2}$ N m; **(e)** No; **(f)** Yes, $25\sqrt{3}$ N m.

EXERCISE 3B

1 $\sqrt{53}$ N.

2 13 N.

3 $\sqrt{34}$ N.

4 $\sqrt{85}$ N.

5 $\sqrt{211}$ N.

6 $\sqrt{234}$ or $3\sqrt{26}$ N.

7 $\sqrt{174}$ N.

8 $\sqrt{45}$ or $3\sqrt{5}$ N.

9 $\sqrt{104}$ N, $y = 5x - 10$.

10 $\sqrt{50}$ or $5\sqrt{2}$ N, $7y = x + 5$.

11 $\sqrt{212}$ or $2\sqrt{53}$ N, $14y = 4x - 1$.

12 **(a)** 13 N, $y = \dfrac{70}{13}$;   **(b)** $2\sqrt{10}$ N, $3y + x + 39 = 0$.

16 $x = 1$, $y = 2$, b.

17 3 N, 1 N, 12 N m.

18 10 N, 11 N m anticlockwise.

19 $\sqrt{17}$ N, 28.5 N m anticlockwise.

20 $\sqrt{101}$ N, 12 N m anticlockwise.

21 19.6 N, $38\frac{2}{3}$ N m anticlockwise.

EXERCISE 3C

1 $\tan^{-1} 0.4 = 21.8°$.

2 $\tan^{-1}\frac{3}{7} = 23.2°$.

3 $\tan^{-1}\dfrac{4r}{h}$.

4 $h = 10l$.

5 **(b)** $\dfrac{40}{11}l$;   **(c)** $\dfrac{1}{4}$.

6 (a) $\dfrac{54}{11}l$; **(b)** $\dfrac{2}{9}$.

10 (a) 1.96 N; **(b)** 3.92 N, 0.4.

11 2.45 N, 4.36 N.

12 6 m.

13 26.57°, 18.43°, 5.71°.

14 60°.

15 To $\frac{13}{14}$ths of its length.

17 (b) No change.

18 (a) $P = \dfrac{\mu mg}{\sin\theta - \mu\cos\theta}$;

(c) No change as not dependent on the mass.

4 Frameworks

EXERCISE 4A

| **1** | *AB* | Tension | 11.5 N |
| | *BC* | Compression | 23.1 N. |

| **2** | *RQ* | Tension | 13.1 N |
| | *PQ* | Compression | 8.39 N. |

| **3** | *SQ* | Tension | 60.0 N |
| | *SR* | Compression | 52.0 N. |

| **4** | *AB* | Tension | 25.9 N |
| | *BC* | Compression | 36.6 N. |

| **5** | *PQ* | Tension | 14.6 N |
| | *QR* | Compression | 22.4 N. |

| **6** | *DE* | Tension | 31.6 N |
| | *EF* | Compression | 115 N. |

| **7** | *RS* | Compression | 269 N |
| | *RQ* | Compression | 220 N. |

| **8** | *AB* | Compression | 139 N |
| | *BC* | Compression | 139 N. |

| **9** | *DE* | Compression | 103 N |
| | *EF* | Compression | 52.1 N. |

| **10** | *XY* | Compression | 17.6 N |
| | *XZ* | Compression | 6.95 N. |

EXERCISE 4B

1
PQ	Tension	$159\frac{1}{4}$ N
QR	Tension	147 N
PS	Compression	147 N
QS	Compression	$61\frac{1}{4}$ N
SR	Compression	245 N

2 **(a)** AB, BD and BE 200 N, CD and CE 115 N, DE 231 N;
   (b) All except DE.

3 **(a)** AB 50 N, BD, BE, DC, CE and DE 28.9 N;
   (b) All except DE.

4 AB 40 N tie, BC 40 N tie, BD 0, CD $20\sqrt{5}$ N strut.

5 $R = S = 125$ N
   $AB = AF = 200$ N
   $BC = EF = 250$ N
   $CD = DE = 217$ N
   $BD = DF = 50$ N
   $BF = 87$ N.

6 $R = S = 125$ N
   $AB = CD = 144$ N
   $AE = DE = 72$ N
   $BE = CE = 29$ N
   $BC = 87$ N.

7 $P = Q = 250$ N
   $AB = DE = 289$ N
   $AG = EF = 144$ N
   $BC = CD = 231$ N
   $BG = DF = 173$ N
   $CG = CF = 115$ N
   $GF = 289$ N.

8 **(a)** $R = S = 15$ kN;
   (b) $AB = DE = 30$ kN
      $AF = EF = 26$ kN
      $BF = DF = CF = 10$ kN
      $BC = CD = 20$ kN.

9 **(a)** $R = 167$ N, $S = 133$ N;
   (b) $AB = 333$ N, $BC = 267$ N, $BD = 115$ N, $BE = 231$ N,
      $DE = 173$ N, $AE = 289$ N, $CD = 231$ N.

10 **(a)** 2000 N;
   (b) AB $2000\dfrac{\sqrt{3}}{3}$N tension, AD $2000\dfrac{\sqrt{3}}{3}$N tension,

   DE $1000\dfrac{\sqrt{3}}{3}$N compression;

(c) *AB* and *BC*;

(d) 2650 N.

11 (b) *AB* 3000 N tension, *BC* $1000\sqrt{3}$ N tension.

12 (a) Light rods, Smooth joints; (b) 50 N;
   (c) $AB = 25\sqrt{2}$ N, $AD = 75\sqrt{2}$, N, $AC = 50$ N, $CD = 25\sqrt{2}$ N.
   (d) *AB* and *AC*.

5 Momentum and collisions in one dimension

EXERCISE 5A

1 (a) 0.72 N s; (b) 19 444 N s.

2 (a) 1.2 N s; (b) 1.76 N s.

3 400 000 N s.

4 (a) 5.42 m s^{-1}; (b) 4.2 m s^{-1}; (c) 2.41 N s.

5 485 N s.

6 (a) 9000 N; (b) 6000 N.

7 3.74 m s^{-1}, 0.713 m.

8 (a) 1.28 N s; (b) 12.8 N; (c) 0.128 s.

9 (a) 2.13 N; (b) 3.2 N.

10 9.1%.

11 (a) 1.022 N s, 0.6464 N s, 0.4088 N s;
   (b) Reduced by 63.2% each time;
   (c) 5.12 cm.

12 (a) $m\sqrt{2g}(\sqrt{h} + \sqrt{H})$;
   (b) $\dfrac{m\sqrt{2g}(\sqrt{h} + \sqrt{H})}{T}$;
   (c) $\dfrac{m\sqrt{2g}(\sqrt{h} + \sqrt{H})}{T} + mg$.

EXERCISE 5B

1 (a) 0.625; (b) 3.125 m s^{-1}.

2 (a) 6.3 m s^{-1}; (b) 2.025 m.

3 (a) 1.45 m s^{-1}; (b) 10.8 cm.

4 (a) 13.1 m s^{-1}; (b) 8.75 m.

5 0.816.

6 25.9 cm.

7 $H = \dfrac{h}{e^2}$.

8 0.837.

9 $e = \sqrt{\dfrac{h}{H}}$.

10 (a) $m\sqrt{gH}(1 + \sqrt{2})$; **(b)** $\dfrac{1}{\sqrt{2}}$.

EXERCISE 5C

1 (a) 0.75 N s; **(b)** 4 m s^{-1}.

2 2 m s^{-1}.

3 (a) $v_A = 4.25$ m s^{-1}, $v_B = 6.25$ m s^{-1};
 (b) $v_B = 4$ m s^{-1}, $e = 0.25$; **(c)** $m_A = \dfrac{30}{7}$ kg, $e = \dfrac{3}{7}$.

4 (a) $v_A = 1.8$ m s^{-1}, $v_B = 3.8$ m s^{-1};
 (b) $v_B = 7.5$ m s^{-1}, $m_B = 2.29$ kg; **(c)** $m_A = 9$ kg, $e = \dfrac{1}{6}$.

5 (a) Speed of A reduced to half that before the collision.
 Speed of B is $\dfrac{3}{2}$ times original speed of A;

 (b) $e = \dfrac{1}{3}$.

6 $e > 0.6$.

7 $e = \dfrac{4}{9}$.

8 A 0.223 m s^{-1}, B 0.246 m s^{-1}, C 1.53 m s^{-1}.

9 $\dfrac{18u}{5}$.

10 $\dfrac{6u}{5}$, $3mu$.

11 $e = \dfrac{1}{2}$.

12 $2u$, $\dfrac{2}{3}$, u, $\dfrac{a}{2}$.

13 (a) u in the opposite direction; **(b)** $\dfrac{4}{5}$, u, $\dfrac{4u}{3}$, $\dfrac{1}{9}$.

6 Momentum and collisions in two dimensions

EXERCISE 6A

1 (a) $(-7.07 \times 10^7\mathbf{i} - 7.07 \times 10^7\mathbf{j})$ N s;
 (b) $(2.55\mathbf{i} + 2.55\mathbf{j})$ N s;
 (c) $(-410\mathbf{i} - 1130\mathbf{j})$ N s.

2 $(0.6\mathbf{i} - 0.8\mathbf{j})$ N s.

3 $(13\mathbf{i} + 25\mathbf{j})$ m s^{-1}.

4 $(3\mathbf{i} + 4\mathbf{j})$ N s.

5 $(0.6\mathbf{i} + 0.2\mathbf{j})$ N s.

6 $(2\mathbf{i} + \mathbf{j})$ N s.

7 **(a)** 3 N s; **(b)** 126.9°.

8 5.41 N s, 123.7° to original velocity.

9 **(a)** 2.4 N s; **(b)** 6.25 m s^{-1}; **(c)** 50.2°.

10 $mu\sqrt{5}$.

11 7.89 N s, 77.5° to y axis.

12 **(a)** 2 N s; **(b)** 120°; **(c)** 2.5 N.

13 11.4 N s, 5.36 N s.

14 2.57 N s, 0.202 N s.

EXERCISE 6B

1 $M = \dfrac{3m}{7}$.

2 $(2.6\mathbf{i} + 0.2\mathbf{j})$ m s^{-1}.

3 25.6 km h^{-1}, 43.0° east of north.

4 1.24 m s^{-1}.

5 $U = 4$, $W = 4$.

6 0.177 m s^{-1} at 30° above horizontal.

7 1.07 m s^{-1}, 30.1°.

8 **(a)** 90.0 m s^{-1}; **(b)** 36.9° to the vertical.

9 3.51 m s^{-1}, 75° to the wall.

10 10.8°, 2.61 m s^{-1}.

11 $(4.92\mathbf{i} + 16.72\mathbf{j})$ m s^{-1}.

EXERCISE 6C

1 **(a)** 0.6; **(b)** 1.6 N s.

2 **(a)** 53.1°; **(b)** 0.769.

3 **(a)** 3.30 m s^{-1} at 31.0° to the wall; **(b)** 0.905 N s.

4 **(a)** 5.14 m s^{-1} at 34.8° to the wall; **(b)** 0.324.

5 8.54 m s^{-1} at 35.8° above horizontal.

6 **(a)** $\dfrac{1}{3}$; **(b)** $\dfrac{2\sqrt{3}}{3}mu$.

7 $\frac{3}{4}$, 0.110 m.

8 37.8°.

9 1.22*h*.

10 $\tan \gamma = \dfrac{1 + e + e^2}{2e^2}$.

EXERCISE 6D

1 $(3.04\mathbf{i} + 4\mathbf{j})$ m s^{-1}, $(4.84\mathbf{i} + 3\mathbf{j})$ m s^{-1}.

2 $(3\mathbf{i} + 5\mathbf{j})$ m s^{-1}, $(4\mathbf{i} + 7\mathbf{j})$ m s^{-1}.

3 5.9°.

4 14.7°.

5 $v\left(\dfrac{1 - e}{2}\right) \cos \theta \mathbf{i} + v \sin \theta \mathbf{j}$, $v\left(\dfrac{1 + e}{2}\right) \cos \theta \mathbf{i}$.

6 **(a)** $\cos \beta = \dfrac{m_B v_B}{m_A u}$; **(b)** $v_A = \dfrac{u\sqrt{3}}{2}$, $v_B = \dfrac{u}{10}$; **(c)** $\dfrac{1}{5}$.

7 75.4°

8 20.2 m s^{-1}, 38.2°.

9 4.61 m s^{-1}.

10 **(b)** 0.6685*u*.

11 **(a)** $-\dfrac{1}{2}u \cos \theta(3e + 1)$, $\dfrac{1}{2}u \cos \theta(3e - 1)$; **(c)** $\tan \theta = \sqrt{\dfrac{7}{128}}$.

12 **(a)** $e = 1$; **(b)** 90°.

13 **(b)** 4*mu*.

Exam style practice paper

1 **(a)** T^{-1}; **(b)** $\dfrac{3}{2}$.

2 **(a)** $R = \dfrac{W}{3}$, $S = \dfrac{2W}{3}$;

   (b) AB $\dfrac{2\sqrt{3}W}{9}$, tension, AG $\dfrac{4\sqrt{3}W}{9}$, compression, BG $\dfrac{4\sqrt{3}W}{9}$, tension.

3 **(b)** 1.4 m s^{-1};
   (c) The spheres move in the same direction along the line, B has
      speed 0.42 m s^{-1} and C has speed 0.98 m s^{-1};
   (d) A collides with B.

4 **(a)** 055.6°; **(b)** 2218 hours, 124 km.

5 **(c)** $\mu < \dfrac{5a \sin \alpha}{5a \cos \alpha + 12b \sin \alpha}$.

6 $v_A = 3.21$ m s^{-1}, $v_B = 4.62$ m s^{-1}.